MARINE ENGINEER
AND INSTALLAT

ned on or b

MARINE STEAM TURBINES

by

K. M. B. DONALD,
B.Sc., C.Eng., M.I.Mech.E., F.I.Mar.E.

THE INSTITUTE OF MARINE ENGINEERS

Published for the Institute of Marine Engineers

by

Marine Media Management Ltd.
76 Mark Lane, London EC3R 7JN
(England Reg. No. 1100685)

ISBN:0 900976 58 6

Printed in England by J. W. Arrowsmith Ltd., Bristol

CONTENTS

Page

1. Introduction   1

PART I
Existing Designs and Future Developments

2. The Revival of the Marine Steam Turbine in 1962   2

3. Types of Turbine   5

4. A Brief Recapitulation of Basic Steam Turbine Theory   7

5. A General Description of the Cross-Compounded Marine Steam Turbine   13

6. A Description of Some Types of Turbine in Service   17

7. A Review of the Immediate Future   63

PART II
Inspection, Trouble-shooting and Case Histories

8. An External Examination of the Turbine when Running   75

9. An Internal Examination of the Turbine   76

10. An Introduction to Blade and Wheel Vibration   82

11. Rough Running of Turbine Machinery   100

12. The Balancing of Flexible Rotors   103

13. Measurements and Limits of Vibration   109

14. Technical Investigation Case Histories   114

ACKNOWLEDGEMENTS

This book is largely based on a paper which the author wrote for the Lloyd's Register of Shipping Technical Association during the 1971–72 Session. It has been up-dated with the most recent information from the manufacturers listed hereunder, to whom he is most grateful. Unfortunately, in a fast-changing technological world, some of the information changes almost before the printers ink is dry on the paper. Nevertheless, the bulk of the contents is based on long and sometimes hard-won experience which hopefully should not date so rapidly.

He would like to thank all his colleagues, past and present, within Lloyd's Register of Shipping, and the many friends outside who are, or were, connected with the marine industry, who have all contributed to his knowledge and experience over many years. In particular, he would like to thank the Committee of Lloyd's Register of Shipping and Mr. B. Hildrew, C.B.E., M.Sc., C.Eng., D.I.C., the Technical Director, for their kind permission to publish this book. To Mr. Hildrew again, his thanks for setting him on the road during the happy days in E.I.D., as it was then designated.

To the Lloyd's Register Technical Association, and their then President, Mr. A. R. Hinson, C.Eng., who gave their kind permission to print the contents of the paper in book form.

To Dr. S. Archer, C.G.I.A. (h.c.), C.Eng., who edited the original paper, and many who contributed in various ways.

To Mr. J. Cashman, Senior Executive in charge of "Register Book" for his help and for that of his colleagues in the compilation of the statistical information.

To the manufacturers of marine steam turbines throughout the world a special thanks for their most generous help in providing so much information for publication, and for their good wishes for success with the book.

They are:
1) Blohm & Voss A.G, Hamburg, West Germany.
2) De Laval Turbine Inc., New Jersey, USA.
3) General Electric Company, Massachusetts, USA.
4) GEC Turbine Generators, Manchester, UK.
5) Hitachi Zosen, Osaka, Japan.
6) Kawasaki Heavy Industries Ltd., Kobe, Japan.
7) Stal-Laval Turbin A.B, Finspong, Sweden.

Finally, to his wife, Kathleen, for enduring his absence from home when he was many years globe trotting with the Technical Investigation Department, and with the Advanced Engineering Section in more recent years plus the endless months of burning the midnight oil in preparing technical papers, and up-dating this book.

AIM OF BOOK

This book has been written for sea-going engineers who rarely get the chance to look inside the casing of the steam turbines they control, and for designers of steam turbines who never have the opportunity to operate their propulsion machinery in service.

It is also a reference book for owners, shipbuilders, engine builders, and all who manage or operate shipping.

1. INTRODUCTION

Readers will probably be aware of the increasing numbers of steam turbines selected to power tankers and container ships in recent years.

More so today than in previous years these vessels represent large capital investments to their owners.

It is important, therefore, that marine engineers should be acquainted with the latest types of turbine which will be in operation during the 1970's and some of the problems which are common to turbines of all types.

As the title suggests the subject matter is almost entirely concerned with the steam turbine as a prime mover. Where applicable brief reference is made to gearing, boilers, condensers and steam cycles, but obviously these components of the total installation could not all be dealt with in the same detail.

The contents of this book are divided into two main sections.

The first part examines briefly the reasons for the steam turbine revival, reviews the main types in use or on the market, and finally assesses the prospects for the steam turbine in the immediate future based on orders received, and concludes with a brief outline of the developments taking place for the more distant future.

The second part deals with some of the faults which should be looked for when the casing is opened up, introduces the subject of blade and wheel vibration, continues with an examination of the reasons for rotor vibration, modal balancing of flexible rotors, and the limits of vibration specified by various manufacturers. In conclusion some case histories of turbine investigations are presented.

2. THE REVIVAL OF
THE MARINE STEAM TURBINE

The revival of the steam turbine as a marine propulsion unit probably began as early as November, 1962, when the General Electric Company, of America, announced their MST-13 single-plane design which it was claimed was cheaper to install and required less headroom than previous designs.

In early 1963 Stal-Laval, of Sweden, introduced their AP (Advanced Propulsion) series which was also a single-plane arrangement. The most significant difference in Stal-Laval's design was the adoption of overhung epicyclic gearing in place of the conventional parallel gearing for the first reduction.

It was probably the introduction of these two new concepts in marine turbine design coupled with the improvements in fuel rates and the better propulsive efficiency obtained by using low-speed propellers which broke through the barriers of the "diesel complex" as it has been called. It has been estimated, for example, that a reduction in propeller rev/min from 100 to 60 for a 500 000 dwt tanker would reduce the power requirement by some 7·5 MW, equivalent to about 16 per cent.

Obviously, the increase in size of tankers, and the advent of the fast container vessels was foreseen by these companies in the early years with the recognition that large power requirements would follow.

TABLE I(a)

Vessels Completed		
	BHP	per cent
Diesel total	3 385 870	93·15
Turbine	shp	
Mitsubishi	84 000	2·31
G.E. (USA)	79 000	2·17
Westinghouse	46 500	1·28
Stal-Laval	24 000	0·66
De Laval	15 500	0·43
Turbine total	249 000	6·85
Diesel and turbine total	3 634 870	100·00

TABLE I(b)

Vessels Launched		
	BHP	per cent
Diesel total	3 727 200	88·89
Turbine	shp	
G.E. (USA)	223 000	5·32
Mitsubishi	101 000	2·41
Westinghouse	50 500	1·21
Kawasaki	42 800	1·02
Stal-Laval	24 000	0·57
C.E.M.	15 000	0·36
Canadian G.E.	9 000	0·22
Turbine total	465 300	11·11
Diesel and turbine total	4 192 500	100·00

If one compares Table I(a) and I(b) which were published in September, 1967, of the total power of all ocean-going ships completed or launched in the same period between 1st January to 30th June, 1967, the percentage of turbine power in ships launched is almost doubled, and these power units would have been ordered in 1964, 1965 and 1966. In Table II, which refers to vessels ordered in the same period in 1967, the percentage of turbine power has increased five-fold over the vessels completed. This was largely due to a preference shown by owners for turbine installations in vessels of

TABLE II

Vessels Ordered		
	BHP	per cent
Diesel total	2 684 505	67·90
Turbine	shp	
G.E. (USA)	363 000	9·18
Stal-Laval	324 000	8·20
Mitsubishi	230 000	5·82
A.E.G.	112 000	2·83
Kawasaki	90 000	2·28
Ansaldo	15 000	0·38
Undisclosed	135 000	3·41
Turbine total	1 269 000	32·10
Diesel and turbine total	3 953 505	100·00

100 000 tons deadweight and over. It is also of interest to note the ascending positions of the two companies mentioned above, particularly Stal-Laval which bears out the supposition that the two new designs were timed to meet an expected need.

3. TYPES OF TURBINE

It is difficult these days to know which manufacturer is building turbines of original design, or of a type based on a previous licence agreement with slight modifications, or solely under licence with no changes. An attempt has been made to categorize the known manufacturers in Table III, but it should be appreciated that the accuracy of the following cannot be guaranteed.

The following manufacturers' turbines have been selected for illustration and some description based on:
1) The types most likely to be encountered in practice which are also original design concepts such as Stal-Laval, G.E. (USA).
2) Information received from the manufacturers of other original design types such as Kawasaki, De Laval, G.E.C.

TABLE III.—DESIGNERS AND MANUFACTURERS OF MODERN STEAM TURBINES

Country	Manufacturer	Original design	Built solely under licence	Own design based on previous licence	Other remarks
America	G.E. (USA)	yes	—	—	—
	Westinghouse	yes	—	—	—
	De Laval	yes	—	—	—
France	Compagnie Electro-Mechanique (C.E.M.)	—	—	—	Ceased all work on marine turbines approx 1965
Germany	A.E.G.	yes	—	—	—
	Blohm & Voss	yes	—	—	—
Japan	Kawasaki Heavy Industries (K.H.I.)	yes	—	—	—
	Mitsubishi Heavy Industries (M.H.I.)	—	Previously Westinghouse and Escher-Wyss	At present Westinghouse (1974)	—
	Ishikawajima-Harinia Heavy Industries (I.H.I.)	—	G.E. (USA) until 1967	At present G.E. (USA) (1974)	—
Sweden	Stal-Laval	yes			
United Kingdom	G.E.C.	yes	—	—	—

5

3) Unique design concepts for the interest value such as Blohm & Voss.

To avoid repitition of description a broad summary of modern HP and LP turbine designs will be outlined (after a brief re-capitulation of some basic steam turbine theory), since, in many respects, all turbines are very similar in basic design today.

4. A BRIEF RECAPITULATION OF BASIC STEAM TURBINE THEORY

4.1. THE PURE IMPULSE STAGE

In a single-stage, pure, impulse turbine, the steam pressure at entry to and exit from the moving blades is equal, the whole expansion having taken place in the fixed nozzles. Pressure energy in front of the nozzles is converted to kinetic energy in the passage of steam through the nozzles. The high-velocity steam leaving the nozzles is then turned in direction by the moving blades, and the change of momentum of the steam produces a force on the blades, and thus a torque on the shaft.

The passage of steam through the nozzles results in some inefficiency due to friction, so not all the potential energy is converted to kinetic energy. Similarly, there is some loss due to friction as the steam passes through the moving blades, which results in reheating of the steam at constant pressure. Finally, therefore, the gross stage efficiency is made up of losses in both nozzles and blades.

4.2. PRESSURE COMPOUNDING

One of the disadvantages of the pure, single-stage, impulse turbine is the high velocity of the steam leaving the moving blades, known as the "leaving loss", which can be as large as eleven per cent of the initial kinetic energy. By arranging for the pressure drop to occur over a number of pure impulse stages in series (known as pressure-compounding), the efficiency can be improved. The velocity of the steam leaving the first stage "carries over" to the next row of nozzles, augmenting the kinetic energy of expansion in the nozzles of that stage, through to the final stage, where again the steam leaves with high velocity, but the "leaving loss" is now only a small part of the total available energy. The "leaving loss" of such a turbine is usually about 2 per cent and is called a "Rateau" turbine.

4.3. VELOCITY COMPOUNDING

If the steam at outlet from the first moving row of an impulse turbine is turned back by a set of fixed blades on to a second row of moving blades, the final steam velocity leaving the second row is greatly reduced.

This is known as velocity compounding. There may be two or three rows of moving blades on a single "wheel", which is referred to as a "Curtis" wheel. At the optimum velocity ratios the gross stage efficiency of the three-row Curtis wheel is less than that of the two-row wheel, and both are less than the single-row impulse wheel, but the advantages of velocity-compounding are that they are more efficient at lower moving blade speeds, can accept much larger heat-drops and are relatively compact in terms of shaft length. These advantages are utilized in the design of both 'astern' turbines and cargo-oil pump turbines, for oil tankers.

Since astern power in most vessels is used for comparatively short periods of time the lower maximum operating efficiency is of little consequence. Curtis wheels are sometimes used as the "control" stage, (first stage) of an HP ahead turbine, so as to quickly reduce the inlet pressure and temperature of the steam before entering the first row of moving blades.

The "control" stage nozzles are often housed in a separate nozzle box (or nozzle belt) so the high pressure and temperature steam at inlet is thus confined to the nozzle box, minimizing any tendency for local thermal distortion of the turbine casing.

The pure impulse wheel is the more common form of "control" stage adopted in most modern marine steam turbine designs because of the higher gross stage efficiency which can be achieved at or near the nominal design conditions.

4.4. PRESSURE-VELOCITY COMPOUNDING

Yet another variation of the pure impulse turbine is the combination of both pressure and velocity compounding, which again is used in some astern turbine designs.

4.5. IMPULSE-REACTION STAGING

Because of the loss of kinetic energy in the moving blades of a pure impulse turbine due to friction, there is a component of force acting on the moving blades in a downstream axial direction, which is termed the "idle" component or "idle" thrust. The situation can be improved with regard to both stage efficiency and axial ("idle") thrust by arranging for a small pressure drop to occur in the moving blades or, by definition, by introducing a small percentage of "reaction". This also adds a "reaction thrust" to the blades, which increases the work done per stage.

In Figs. 1(a) and 1(b) the differences are illustrated on the enthalpy–entropy diagram between the pure impulse stage and the mixed, impulse-reaction stage. The diagrams are somewhat exaggerated to show the point more clearly; in each case AB represents the adiabatic and isentropic heat-drop, and AC, the expansion in the nozzles. CD in Fig. 1(a) is the reheating of the steam at constant pressure in the moving blades,

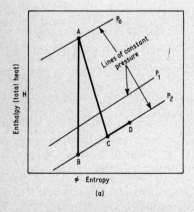
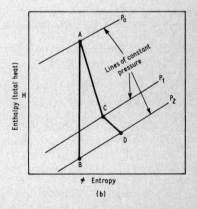

FIG. 1(a).—*Pure impulse.*   FIG. 1(b).—*Impulse-reaction.*

and CD in Fig. 1(b) is the expansion of the steam as it passes through the moving blades. The larger the percentage of reaction, the larger CD becomes in Fig. 1(b).

The significance of the foregoing is the fact that some designers no longer make a specific distinction between impulse or reaction blading, and it is usual to design for varying percentages of reaction (at the mean height) in impulse blading, the percentage increasing towards the HP exhaust end and through the LP turbine of a two cylinder compounded main steam turbine.

There may be pressure-equalizing holes drilled through each wheel in order to reduce the axial thrust due to pressure differences across each wheel. For this reason and to reduced windage losses, some manufacturers provide an axial sealing strip between the moving blades and nozzles at the base or root of the blades, since steam flow through the pressure balance holes represents a parasitic loss if the percentage of reaction is significant.

4.6. HALF-DEGREE OR 50 PER CENT REACTION STAGING

If a "stage" of fixed and moving blades is designed to allow half the heat-drop to occur in the nozzles and half in the moving blades, the stage is often inaccurately referred to simply as a "reaction" stage, whereas it is also partly impulse, since part of the thrust on the blades is obtained from changing the direction of the steam flow. More correctly, it should be referred to as "50 per cent" reaction, or "half degree" reaction staging. It may be more logical to consider the "50 per cent" reaction stage as a special case of impulse-reaction staging in which both the fixed blades and moving blades are of exactly the same aerofoil shape in cross section. This type of blading is used in conjunction with a particular turbine construction known as the "Parsons" turbine. The moving blades are fitted on a solid or drum-type rotor, and the stationary blades are fixed to the inner surface of the casing. The fixed blades act as the "nozzles" and the moving blades obtain their thrust both from turning the steam flow back into the next row of fixed blades, (impulse) and from the "reaction" due to expansion of the steam.

Both the moving and fixed blade tip clearances have to be kept to a minimum to avoid steam leakage over the tips. To prevent any damage to the blades, should the moving blade tips touch the casing or fixed blades touch the rotor, all blade tips are thinned down to a fine edge which will be rubbed away if contact should occur.

4.7. TWISTED AND TAPERED BLADES

The moving blades in the last few stages of an LP turbine are considerably longer than those at the inlet end of the turbine, and in most modern marine steam turbines these blades are tapered and twisted in section along their length. The twist in the blades is necessary to allow for the change in blade and steam velocities from root to tip. In general, the smaller the ratio between the radius to the blade root and the radius to the blade tip (known as the hub/tip ratio) the greater is the change in blade and steam velocities up the length of the blade, which necessitates a change in blade profile from root to tip to avoid the high flow losses associated with "negative" reaction. Although this design of variable-section blade results in a relatively large, flexurally stiff section near the root compared with the tip, the blade is often tapered off from root to tip to achieve a more uniform distribution of the centrifugal stress due to rotation. A typical blade of this design is shown in Fig. 1(c).

The manufacture of such blades presents some formidable machining problems which makes them more expensive to produce than constant-section blades. This is the chief reason for confining variable geometry blades to the last few stages of the LP turbine.

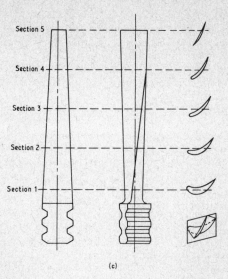

Section 5

Section 4

Section 3

Section 2

Section 1

(c)

FIG. 1(c).—*A typical tapered and twisted blade.*

4.8. "NEGATIVE" REACTION

The degree of reaction R is defined as the ratio of the heat drop in the moving blades to the sum of the heat drops in the nozzles and moving blades, i.e.

$$R = \left[\frac{h_b}{h_N + h_b} \right]$$

The heat drop which takes place in the moving blades is manifest as an expansion of the steam during its passage through the moving blades and thus an increase in steam velocity.

If a compression were to take place at some section along the blade length instead of an expansion, this would be equivalent to work being done on the steam so that the term h_b would become negative, and provided h_N is $>h_b$ the expression for degree of reaction becomes negative at the section considered.

4.9. A BRIEF INTRODUCTION TO "VORTEX" FLOW

The way in which an apparent compression occurs is explained by the vortex flow theory, which can be simplified by saying that because of the oblique angle of the steam flow out of the nozzles the flow path in the gap between the nozzle outlet and moving blade inlet follows a line of flow something like a spiral, and that there must, therefore, be inertia forces set up which cause a variation in steam pressure in the radial direction in the gap.

The radial pressure gradient is not so important in stages where the nozzle height ratio (ratio of radial height "L" of the nozzles to the mean diameter D) is small, but in those stages where the nozzle height ratio is large (such as in the final stages of an LP turbine where the volumetric flow is large) it has a profound effect on the distribution of heat drop in the nozzles and blades.

It follows, therefore, that calculation of the steam conditions at mean blade height (which is the usual method by which the profile of the short blades of constant cross-section are determined) is no longer indicative of the flow characteristics of the longer blades at the exhaust end of an LP turbine.

In Fig. 1(d) which is a section through a "stage" comprising nozzles and moving blades, it is assumed that at entry to the nozzles and at exit from the moving blades the pressure is sensibly constant in a radial direction, i.e. the flow lines are entirely axial in direction relative to the casing. However, as already stated, there is a pressure gradient in the radial direction in the gap between the fixed nozzles and moving blades, so that if the blade profile were calculated on the conditions prevailing at the mean height of the nozzles and blades, based on a pressure drop through the moving blades of $(p_2 - p_3)$, the pressure in the gap near the tip (p_{2T}) would be greater than the mean height inlet pressure (p_2), and the pressure near the root (p_{2R}) would be less than the mean height inlet pressure (p_2).

It is clear, that if the degree of reaction at the moving blade mean height were small, so that the expansion in the moving blades were small, then p_2 would be only slightly greater that p_3, and the inlet pressure at the root (p_{2R}) could in fact be less than (p_3). This would lead to an apparent increase in pressure through a part of the moving blades instead of an expansion, and according to the definition of degree of reaction it would become negative. By the same token the pressure difference $(p_{2T} - p_3)$ at the tip could be greater than that at the mean height, so the degree of reaction would be positive but larger than at the mean height.

Thus, the degree of reaction may increase from negative at the root to a larger positive value at the tip.

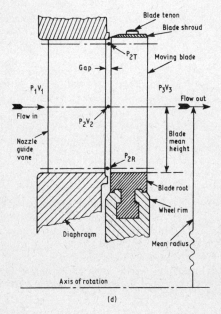

(d)

FIG. 1(d).—*A section through a "stage" comprising nozzles and moving blades.*

To be strictly correct there is not necessarily a flow reversal at the section where negative reaction occurs as one would expect but simply an "over-expansion" of the steam at exit from the nozzles. Such a design of blade would be most inefficient, not only because of the high losses associated with "negative" reaction, but also due to the shock losses at entry to the moving blades due to the incorrect inlet angles of the moving blades.

Modern turbine designs ensure a degree of positive reaction at the root of every moving blade at design conditions to avoid any negative reaction at off-design conditions. All other sections up the blade will have a progressively greater degree of positive reaction.

For the best efficiencies the degree of reaction at the root should be large, increasing still further towards the tip.

There are practical difficulties in achieving this ideal, however, for a large reaction at the root with increasing reaction up the blade could produce high axial loads on the thrust bearing. Again, with the correspondingly higher degree of reaction near the blade tips, steam sealing at the tips would need to be more effective to prevent leakage. Equally important from the practical aspect would be the question of whether the blades would be able to withstand the larger bending forces in addition to the inertia forces due to rotation.

The usual degree of reaction chosen for full power operation is about 0·05 (five per cent) at the root.

From the foregoing example of "degree of reaction" when applied to large LP turbine blades it is not surprising that the usual descriptions "reaction" or "impulse" turbine are not sufficiently definitive, for as has already been stated "reaction" blading is also partly "impulse". Thus a long LP turbine blade may be nearly all "impulse" at the root and nearly all "reaction" at the tip. (80 per cent "reaction" at the tip in some cases.)

4.10. POWER OUTPUT

Broadly speaking, the power which can be developed in a single stage of 50 per cent reaction blades is about half that which can be developed in a single stage pure impulse turbine (for the same moving blade speed) and about one eighth of the power which can be developed in a two-row velocity-compounded impulse stage. It will be appreciated that the velocity-compounded impulse stage is particularly suitable for driving auxiliary machinery such as cargo oil pumps, boiler feed pumps, ballast pumps, etc., having the advantages of being compact, and relatively cheap to manufacture, yet capable of developing high powers.

4.11. EFFICIENCY

With regard to gross stage efficiency, however, the situation is completely reversed, the 50 per cent reaction stage being the most efficient, and the velocity-compound two-row Curtis wheel, and three-row Curtis wheel progressively less efficient. The power ratings of cargo-oil-pump and ballast-pump turbines installed on VLCC has increased quite dramatically from the middle '60s to the early '70s from around 500 shp to about 2500 shp, with projected powers up to 5000 shp. Since the stage efficiency of currently operating two-row Curtis-wheel turbines is only about 60 per cent or less, the advantages outlined above have been overshadowed by considerations of boiler capacity and fuel costs, and manufacturers are having to devise means for improving the efficiencies of the larger capacity cargo-oil pump turbines.

5. A GENERAL DESCRIPTION OF THE CROSS-COMPOUNDED MAIN STEAM TURBINES

Turbine inlet pressures and temperatures are generally in the region of 850 lb/in^2 and 513°C, exhausting to 28·5 in. of mercury in the condenser.

5.1. HIGH PRESSURE TURBINES

The majority of manufacturers have adopted the "Rateau" or pressure-compounded impulse-type turbine design which requires few stages to achieve the necessary heat-drop, enabling short shaft-lengths to be employed, saving in weight and overall length.

Rotors are usually solid-forged and are machined down to form wheels for the attachment of the moving blades. HP turbines may have from 8 to 12 stages, depending upon power requirements, turbine specification and blade height. Each stage except the first comprises a diaphragm containing nozzle guide vanes round the complete 360° circumference, followed by a wheel containing the moving blades.

The wheel and diaphragm impulse-type design enables the shaft diameter to be kept to a minimum thus reducing the area of steam leakage past each diaphragm steam sealing gland. The flexibility of rotors ensures a first critical speed well below the running speed. The first stage may be a single impulse wheel, or a velocity-compounded wheel, called a "Curtis" wheel.

It is usually a larger diameter wheel with fewer nozzles than there are in the diaphragms.

The casings of the HP turbine are cast from an alloy steel made in two halves with either integral or separately supported inlet nozzle chamber on the top or bottom halves. The steam inlet and outlet flanged openings are cast integral with either the top or bottom half, and thick flanges at the horizontal joint are provided for the bolts which hold the top and bottom half casings together.

Bearing housings are bolted to the bottom half casing and each bearing housing is separately supported, being rigidly bolted to the seatings, usually at the aft end. Because of the axial expansion of the casing when hot, means are provided to allow the casing to move forward either by supporting the forward bearing on "panting plates" which are adequately flexible in the fore and aft direction or by supporting the bearing housing on a pedestal with axial keys. The thrust bearing is usually located at the forward, steam inlet end of the casing to locate the axial position of the rotor in the casing and to withstand the axial force exerted by the steam on the blades and rotor.

13

Since the axial clearance between blade tip seals and nozzle diaphragms is generally smaller at the inlet stages than at the outlet stages, the thrust bearing is located at the inlet end of the turbine to minimize differential axial expansion effects. A manufacturer usually has a set of standard "frame sizes" of casing and rotor covering a given maximum power output range. Any power output within that range can be obtained by suitable choice of nozzle and blade heights in the standard frame.

HP turbine blades are usually short and of constant section with no twist, the essential differences are the methods of root fixing used, and the shrouding on the blade tips.

Moving blade profiles are sometimes rounded at the leading edges so that varying angles of steam inlet at off-design conditions do not greatly affect the profile losses.

Journal bearings are short and rather highly loaded to avoid the possibility of oil whirl, but some manufacturers fit anti-whirl bearings as standard practice. There may be a spherical seating of the bearing shell in the housing to permit good bedding of the journal when first installed.

Diaphragms are sealed at the inner radius by means of spring-backed labyrinth glands, while the rims are held tight against circumferential grooves in the casing by the differential pressure across them. They should be strong enough to withstand the pressure without excessive deformation. Stresses are usually greatest at the weakest section in way of the nozzles, and deflections will be greatest at the corners of the inner radius. The two halves should have no clearance at the horizontal joint to allow steam leakage when the two casing halves are bolted together. Generally, diaphragms are of welded construction supported at the horizontal joint to allow concentric expansion at the operating temperature.

5.2. LOW PRESSURE TURBINES

In general there are two basic designs of LP turbine. The conventional single-flow type with down-flow exhaust, and the axial-flow exhaust type commonly used in single-plane arrangements. For high powers, in the region of 60 000 shp and over, the "double-flow" LP turbine may be necessary if exhaust outlet areas required for the large volumetric flow were to result in excessive blade tip speeds, stresses or adverse vibration characteristics. Steam enters at the centre of the casing and flows both forward and aftward, along identical steam paths.

The down-flow exhaust type has an astern turbine outlet facing the ahead turbine outlet with some form of deflector between, whilst the axial-flow exhaust permits both ahead and astern turbines to exhaust in the same axial direction to the condenser.

LP turbines have between seven and nine ahead stages and two or three astern stages.

The first five or six stages of moving blades are the usual constant-section type similar to the HP turbine blades, but there may be +10 to +20 per cent reaction at the mean blade height.

Root fixings vary from one manufacturer to another, but those of the long twisted and tapered blades are usually different from the root fixings further upstream due to the higher centrifugal loads they have to accommodate.

Stellite shields may be fitted to the leading edges of the blades of the last stages to enable higher tip speeds to be employed without excessive damage from water droplet erosion. In addition there are water collection channels between the diaphragms of the last stages which catch the droplets thrown off by the moving blades and drain the water directly to the condenser.

The longer blades may or may not be shrouded or fitted with lacing wires or both, usually depending upon the vibration characteristics of the blades and the type of tip sealing used.

The ahead LP casing is usually of prefabricated construction and the diaphragms in the final stages cast with guide vanes integral.

The thrust bearing will generally be at the aft end because steam is usually admitted via the cross-over pipe at the aft end of the LP turbine where axial steam sealing clearances are smaller.

5.3. ASTERN TURBINES

The astern turbine is generally housed in a separate cast casing within the LP outer casing.

There will generally be two or three astern stages, the first stage being a two-row Curtis wheel followed by single wheel or a second Curtis wheel.

The minimum requirements for astern power are roughly equivalent to about 40 per cent of the maximum ahead power assuming the same inlet conditions and mass-flow.

5.4. REHEAT TURBINES

Fairfield's G.E. (USA), Kawasaki, I.H.I. and a German company are the only manufacturers who have actually supplied reheat turbine installations for marine operation in recent years. All the other manufacturers have reheat designs available if required.

There is a basic resemblance between all the types of reheat HP turbine available and in use, superheated steam entering at the centre of the casing and flowing forward through four or five HP stages out to the reheater and returing again to the middle of the turbine and flowing aftwards through the IP section of six to eight stages. The two flows are separated by a partition in the centre of the casing sealed at the rotor surface by a series of labyrinth glands. Inlet conditions are in the region of 1420 lbs/in^2 and 513°C, reheated to 513°C.

A number of manufacturers offer non-reheat cycles operating at the higher steam conditions of 1420 lbs/in^2 and 513°C and in this way are presenting the advantages of better fuel economy with modest turbine sizes without the complications of reheat.

5.5. TURBINE OUTPUT CONTROL

The first stage of the HP turbine may be a two-row velocity-compounded impulse wheel known as a Curtis wheel, or a single row impulse wheel, the latter being more usual in the ahead turbine, because of its better stage efficiency, the former being employed in the first stage of the astern turbine because its lower efficiency is of less importance than the larger heat-drop which it can accommodate.

There are basically two methods of controlling the power output. The first is throttle control, the second is nozzle group control.

In each case the steam inlet nozzles are housed in a nozzle box which is either separately supported within the casing or cast integral with the casing. The separate nozzle box occupies an arc of probably 100° to 150° and is known as "partial admission".

5.5.1. Throttle Valve Control

This type of control throttles the steam through a valve to a group containing a large number of nozzles, thus reducing the steam pressure at the inlet to the nozzles and reducing the available heat-drop through the turbine. It also decreases the quantity of steam flowing by a reduction in the throttle valve area. The throttle valve may be automatically governed to maintain a constant output at a particular setting by hydraulic feed-back or relay to the valve from a governor operated from the HP or LP turbine shaft.

5.5.2. Nozzle Group Control

Integrally cast steam chests and nozzle belts are the usual feature of nozzle group control because the nozzle arc is divided into a number of separate sections by walls within the nozzle housing, each section containing a "group", or small number of nozzles. One group may be permanently open to the steam admitted from the manoeuvring valve (which would then act as a throttle control valve as mentioned above), each of the other groups having their own inlet valve in the steam chest. There may be up to seven separate groups of nozzles in the steam chest, each with its own valve. When a group valve is fully open it admits an additional quantity of steam at the full steam inlet temperature and pressure, therefore the inlet state point is hardly changed. Thus with the opening up of each group of nozzles a further quantity of steam is admitted which increases the power output without greatly changing the heat-drop through the turbine. On the other hand the distribution of heat-drop across each of the stages down stream of the control stage is more affected by this type of control than with the throttle-valve control method.

With nozzle group control at low powers the LP stages downstream do less work whilst the first and following few stages in the HP turbine do a greater share of work less efficiently.

6. A DESCRIPTION OF SOME TYPES OF TURBINE IN SERVICE

6.1. STAL-LAVAL TURBIN A.B. (Sweden)

At present holding the largest share of the marine turbine market Stal-Laval, more than any other manufacturer, seems to have shown a particular ability not only for originality in design but also for selling their product.

Their present range of AP series frames sizes for the HP and LP turbines and reduction gearing is illustrated in Fig. 2. HP turbine frame sizes above the APH32 range are designed for maximum steam inlet conditions of 80 bar 510°C, designated D500, whereas the lower limits in these frame sizes, designated C500, indicate the maximum power obtainable at the more usual steam inlet conditions of 63 bar, 510°C.

The corresponding LP turbine frame size for a specified power is largely dependent upon the condenser vaccum chosen. In general terms if the condenser pressure at the design condition is chosen to be higher than the standard 0·5 bar, (1½ inches of mercury) the LP turbine exhaust area can be made smaller, and hence blade lengths can be kept within acceptable limits to avoid excessive tip speeds. Stal-Laval have stated that in many instances higher condenser pressures have been specified by owners.

It is of interest to note that Stal-Laval have adopted a new technique for their APL 45 frame size last stage blades. To avert water droplet erosion the axial gap between last row nozzles and moving blades has been increased, which, it is claimed, allows water droplets to accelerate to near steam velocity. Thus the last stage blades are not shielded in the conventional manner but are induction-hardened instead. If service operation of marine turbine units proves to be successful this will be a step forward in saving costly manufacture of last stage blades with erosion shielding.

The reduction gearing frame sizes corresponding to the HP and LP turbines in Fig. 2 are represented by lines of constant torque for standard propeller shaft speeds. Gear frame sizes up to 421 (420 kW per rev/min) are of the same general design as the previous epicyclic primaries/parallel secondaries reduction gearboxes. For higher torques, Stal-Laval have adopted the locked-train gear reduction type in order to limit the bull wheel size.

6.1.1. HP Turbine

The basic layout of the HP turbine is shown in Fig. 3. The main feature of Stal-Laval blading is shown in Fig. 4. The roots are of the side-entry type held in place by indenting the bottom of the bulbous end of the root on both sides of the wheel.

The shroud design is also of particular interest because each blade is machined complete with an integral tip platform which butts against its neighbour to form a

17

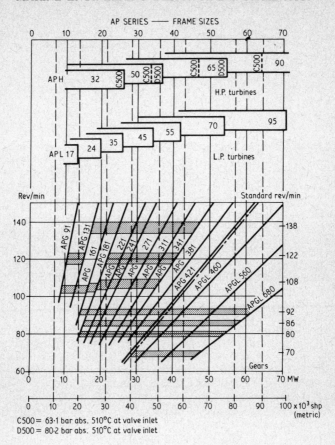

Fig. 2.—*Range of Stal-Laval turbine frame sizes.*

continuous cover. The blades are fitted in the wheel and locked in place. A cover wire is then laid between two radial fins on top of the tip platforms and each fin is rolled over the top of the wire to enclose it completely, as shown in Fig. 4. The ends of the wire meet at the middle of a blade tip platform, so in effect the wire covers the whole circumference as a continuous shroud.

Diaphragms are of welded construction, the guide vanes being inserted into punched slots in an inner and outer steel band. The assembled steel band is then welded onto the body and rim of the diaphragm, as shown in Fig. 5.

6.1.2. LP Turbine

The LP turbine is illustrated in Fig. 6 and shows the two fitted Curtis wheels on the forward end, which are dowelled radially and provided with a retaining ring. The astern inlet pipe has piston sealing rings to permit relative movement between pipe and inlet

FIG. 3.—*Stal-Laval HP turbine*.

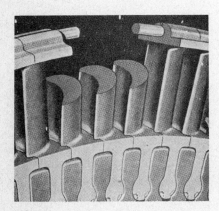

FIG. 4.—*Stal-Laval side-entry blades*.   FIG. 5.—*Stal-Laval manufacture of diaphragms*.

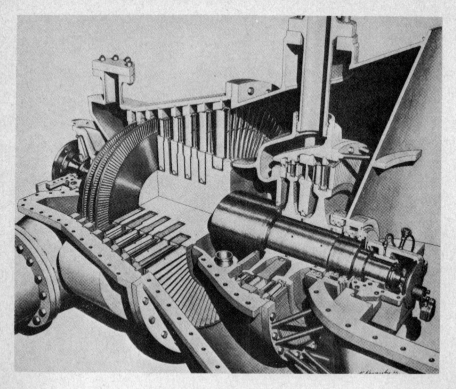

FIG. 6.—*Stal-Laval LP turbine.*

steam belt. Access to the forward LP bearing is possible through an open well between the LP outlet and condenser inlet.

All ahead LP stages have shrouding, the last three rows having tapered and twisted blades with lacing wires fitted at about mid-height. The shrouding on the last rows is based on the same construction mentioned for the HP blades but two smaller, separate and adjacent wires are rolled into the tips instead of one.

The root type is the same construction as the HP blades, the additional strength being obtained by the increased width of the root.

An extra stage would be added to the LP turbine when used in combination with the HP reheat turbine.

6.1.3. Reheat Turbine

Stal-Laval have not, at the time of writing, had any orders for reheat turbines, but have a design available should the market trend change. Illustrated in Fig. 7 the general layout is very similar to all designs of marine reheat turbines on the market and in operation.

The centre inlet arrangement gives the least possible temperature and pressure differences across the casing shell, and partition wall. One important feature of a reheat

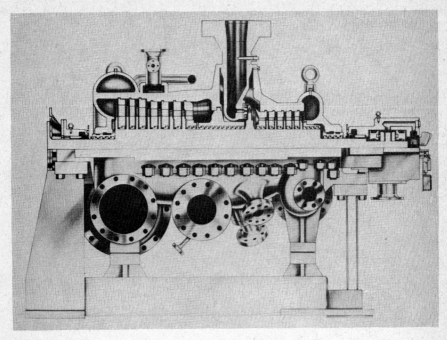

FIG. 7.—*Stal-Laval reheat HP-IP turbine.*

turbine of this sort is that the thermal inertia of the casing and rotor should be as nearly equal as possible by suitable distribution of masses to reduce the relative expansions to a minimum as well as the effect of thermal gradients during transient conditions (i.e. both heating up and cooling down).

The thrust bearing is located at the forward end of the rotor so during transient conditions, when heating up or cooling down, the differential expansion between the rotor and casing will be such that when heating up the HP section (forward six stages) will tend to close up axially, reducing axial tip sealing clearances while the IP section (aft seven stages) will tend to move away axially from the diaphragms increasing axial tip clearances. The reverse would occur when reducing power.

Since there is a small amount of "reaction" designed into the impulse stages large clearances at the tip seals to accommodate the differential expansions would result in some loss of stage efficiency. Stal-Laval have designed the tip seals such that a thin steel strip fixed to the outlet of the nozzle diaphragms at the outer periphery of the nozzles, and inclined at about 45° to the plane of the diaphragms seals radially onto the top surface of the moving blade shrouds, thus allowing axial movements of the rotor without substantially altering the sealing clearance.

The same problem would arise with regard to labyrinth gland seals, in both the atmospheric glands and the interstage glands. Stal-Laval employ the Vernier-type labyrinth gland on such turbines, which permits axial movement without loss of sealing.

Contra-flow reduces the net axial force on the thrust bearing to a large extent, provided the two inlet pressures remain within certain limits.

Since Stal-Laval have had no operating experience with this turbine, very little can be contributed in this respect.

6.1.4. Epicyclic Gearbox Mounting

The gearcase construction is such that the main casing which houses the main wheel and secondary pinions is supported on only four pads, two being fixed under the main wheel bearings and the other two in the middle of the port and starboard sides. The main wheel housing carries the total weight of all the epicyclic gearing and conventional secondary train.

The main gearbox housing may be spring-loaded at the corners to permit adjustment of the pinion bearing centres by flexing the main housing to suit the best gear tooth contact area on each pinion if needed.

When erected in the shop, the corner "springing" loads are adjusted to give full tooth contact area. When mounted in the vessel, the corner "springing" loads are set to the shop-erection values. If, after full power trials, the gear contact areas are not evenly distributed, further adjustment of the corner "springs" can be made to obtain the specified gear tooth contact length.

TABLE IV—STEAM CYCLES OFFERED BY STAL-LAVAL LTD*

Power		32 000 shp (British)/32 440 shp (metric)			
Cycle characteristics		3B	4B	5B	5BR
Superheat pressure	psig (ata)	918/65·6	918/65·6	1173/83·6	1480/105·1
Superheat temperature	°F (°C)	955/513	955/513	955/513	955/513
Reheat pressure	psig (ata)	—	—	—	316/23·2
Reheat temperature	°F (°C)	—	—	—	955/513
Feed temperature	°F (°C)	288/142	381/194	408/209	430/221
Uptake temperature	°F (°C)	33/167	265/130	265/130	265/130
Boiler efficiency	—	0·883	0·900	0·900	0·900
Condenser pressure	in Hg (ata)	1·5/0·0517	1·5/0·0517	1·5/0·0517	1·5/0·0517
HP feed heaters	—	—	1	2	2
LP feed heaters	—	3	3	3	3
Generator drive	—	Sep.	Sep	Sep.	Sep.
Generator load	kW	500	500	500	500
Feed pump drive	—	Sep.	Sep.	Sep.	Sep.
Feed pump power	kW	375	380	470	500
Evaporator cooling	—	Cond.	Cond.	Cond.	Cond.
Evaporator load	lb/h (kg/h)	3090/1400	3090/1400	3090/1400	3090/1400
Lub. oil cooling	—	Sea W.	Sea W.	Sea W.	Sea W.
Air ejector	—	Steam	Steam	Steam	Steam
Cooling water circ.	—	Scoop	Scoop	Scoop	Scoop
Overall thermal efficiency	—	0·308	0·316	0·322	0·338
Fuel oil rate	g/shph	201	196	192	182

Steam cycle characteristics:—
3, 4, 5: Number of feed heaters.   R: Reheat.
B: Back pressure turbine generator drive.
Calorific value of fuel 18 500 BThU's/lb.

* By courtesy of Stal-Laval Ltd.

6.1.5. Steam Cycles

The series of cycles offered by Stal-Laval is set out in Table IV. The 3B and 4B cycle is conventional by today's standards, the 3B having economizer and steam-air heater, and the 4B with gas-air heater.

The feed pump and generator are separate self-contained turbine-driven units.

The 5B cycle has a second high-pressure feed heater which is justified at the higher main steam conditions.

In general terms Stal-Laval would recommend:
a) Separate turbo-generators of the back pressure type.
b) Condensate cooled distillers rather than lubricating oil coolers.
c) Separate turbine-driven feed pumps.
d) Scoop circulation of sea water to the condenser.

Their experience has shown that the $1\frac{1}{2}$-boiler system is most suitable for tankers, but twin boilers should be installed in container ships requiring high availability, and in all ships with twin-screw installations.

Scoop circulation appears to be in use, more by tanker vessels than by the fast container ships.

6.1.6. Lubrication

The lubricating oil system for AP units is made up of an external and internal system.

The external system shown in Fig. 8, containing pumps, coolers, filters, etc., are all optional items.

The internal system shown in Fig. 9 which is built into the unit, containing gravity tank, engine-driven oil pump and oil distribution pipework. The oil system is a direct feed pressure circuit taking oil from the sump and distributing it through orifices to the bearings and gear meshes. Should the external pump system fail, the main steam supply is shut off automatically and the main engine-driven pump, in combination with the gravity feed tank on top of the gear casing, will continue to supply oil to the bearings for an estimated 10 to 20 minutes. During that time the standby oil pump should be started or the turbine brought to rest on astern steam.

As far as is known, however, the guardian valve and astern valve must be opened by hand.

6.2. General Electric Company [G.E. (USA)]

The General Electric Company (USA) is one of the largest manufacturers of marine steam turbines in the world today. For some years they have marketed the MST-13 and MST-14 ranges of turbines to a maximum of 45 000 shp, and more recently have extended the range from 45 000 shp to 120 000 shp, designated the MST-19.

Two basic sizes of HP turbine, and three basic sizes of LP turbine cover the power range of the MST-19 type. In Fig. 10 the block diagram illustrates the series of combinations. For each of the two power ranges, 45 000 shp to 70 000 shp and 70 000 shp to 120 000 shp, non-reheat and reheat cycles are provided. This increases the basic HP design to four, combined with three basic LP turbine designs of differing last stage annulus area. The last LP design shown in Fig. 10 is a double-flow type with final stage annulus of 50 square feet.

By suitably combining the standard frames in the usual cross-compound arrangement and making the proper choice of nozzle areas in the flow path, any intermediate

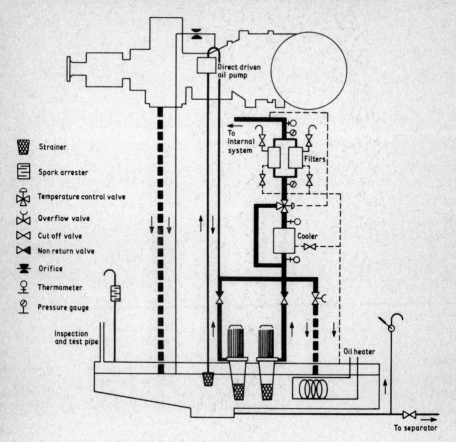

Strainer

Spark arrester

Temperature control valve

Overflow valve

Cut off valve

Non return valve

Orifice

Thermometer

Pressure gauge

Inspection
and test pipe

Direct driven
oil pump

To
internal
system

Filters

Cooler

Oil heater

To separator

FIG. 8.—*Stal-Laval external lubricating oil system.*

power between 45 000 shp and 120 000 shp can be obtained with various levels of thermal performance.

For non-reheat cycles in the 45 000 shp to 70 000 shp range, steam inlet conditions of 850 lbs/in² and 510°C have been chosen as the most suitable for the merchant marine industry. In the higher power range of 70 000 shp to 120 000 shp steam conditions of 1450 lbs/in² and 510°C are selected for both reheat and non-reheat cycles (with reheat to 510°C). These higher inlet conditions are to a large extent determined by size limitations of boilers, pipework and valves, etc.

6.2.1. HP Turbine

The first of the HP turbine frame sizes shown in Fig. 10 is illustrated in detail in Fig. 11. The sequentially operated nozzle-group control valves are located in the integrally-cast steam chest on the top half and the nozzle box is cast directly beneath the steam chest, with provision for nozzle arcs of up to 220°. The nozzle box projects slightly below the horizontal joint on both sides but is quite independent of the bottom half.

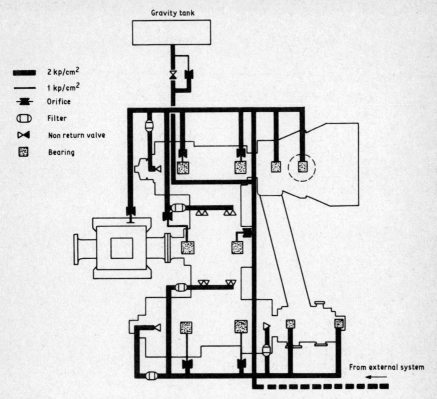

FIG. 9.—*Stal-Laval internal lubricating oil system.*

The concept of the bar-lift, sequentially-opening nozzle valves is one which the manufacturer has employed for many years and which gives greater efficiency in part-load operation as well as at the higher powers. There can be up to seven separate nozzle group control valves with valve stems of different length depending upon the sequence of valve lift required. Each of the valve stems is free to slide in a common horizontal bar, all being located in the chamber of the steam chest. Two bar-lifting rods pass through the steam chest from control gear on top of the chest and by raising the bar each nozzle-group valve is opened in turn according to its stem-length.

The single astern turbine control valve is hung on the end of the steam chest opposite the main steam inlet whilst the hydraulic valve-operating gear is located on the forward bearing pedestal.

Steam bleed pipes are located on the bottom half. The steam outlet is vertically upwards to the cross-over pipe, which is said to give greater flexibility.

6.2.2. LP Turbine

The LP turbine at the top of the group of three LP frame sizes in Fig. 10 is shown in more detail in Fig. 12. Steam entry is at the top of the aft end flowing into a full admission inlet belt. The inner cylinders are cast whilst the outer cylinder is prefabricated.

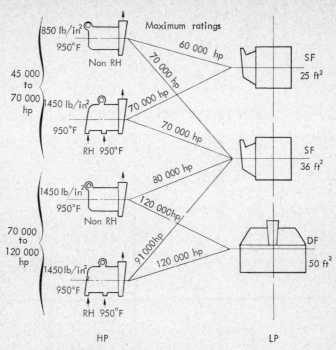

FIG. 10.—*Range of G.E. (USA) M.S.T.19 turbine frame sizes for higher horsepowers.*

The spaces between the inner and outer casing are available as bled steam chambers. On the bottom half it will be seen that water collection channels between the diaphragms of the last four stages are drained through orificed plugs into a common gulley which is led directly to the condenser. (Obviously these orifices must always be maintained clear of debris.)

The astern turbine stages comprise a two-row Curtis wheel and one impulse stage. The inlet steam belt is supported at the centreline with the steam inlet at the top incorporating a slip-joint construction using piston-ring seals.

An axial-exhaust LP turbine is also manufactured for applications requiring the single-plane cross-compound arrangement.

It will be seen from the diagram that the thrust collar is exceptionally thick. This is to enable some machining of the faces to be undertaken in the case of surface damage without reducing the collar thickness necessary for maximum design thrust.

6.2.3. Reheat Turbine

The high pressure reheat turbine which the manufacturers have designed and installed in at least nine vessels is shown in Fig. 13. Steam condititions are 1450 lbs/in² at 510°C inlet, 510°C reheat. The inlet is in the middle of the casing through the ahead inlet control at the top of the casing flowing through a single row impulse wheel and four Rateau stages to the outlet at the forward end bottom-half cylinder. The reheated steam enters at the bottom directly into a full admission diaphragm and flows aft through five Rateau stages to the outlet on the bottom half. The thrust bearing is at the forward end

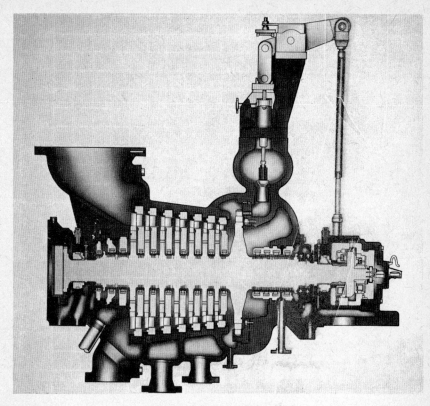

FIG. 11.—*G.E. (USA) HP turbine.*

in the bearing pedestal which is dowelled to the half ring integral with the bottom-half casing. Notice the high pressure partition wall and labyrinth seals in the middle of the shaft.

6.2.4. Control

Both HP and LP turbines are provided with governing devices which prevent overspeed. The governors are set to begin closing the inlet valves at about 102 per cent of the rated speed, and are completely closed at 108 per cent of the rated speed.

The various trip devices, including low bearing oil pressure, etc., close only the ahead valves, enabling steam to be applied to the astern turbine to act as a brake. Overspeed limits apply to both ahead and astern rotation when bridge control is operative.

Higher horsepowers and steam flows would require larger valves and significantly larger lifting forces. The conventional control gear uses lubricating oil boosted to about 55 lbs/in^2, to lift the control valves. To reduce the size of pistons required for the higher powered turbines the manufacturers have elected to increase hydraulic pressures to 1100 lbs/in^2, by employing a variable displacement radial-piston pump. A separate oil

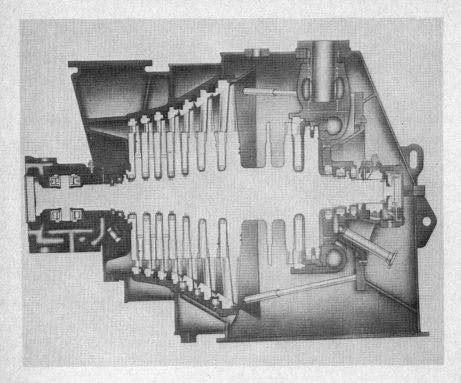

FIG. 12.—*G. E. (USA) LP turbine.*

reservoir is provided for the pump to maintain a high degree of cleanliness in the hydraulic system. For future applications a fire resistant fluid is planned, but for the present a regular petroleum oil is in use.

6.2.5. Astern Power

The manufacturers have already considered the astern power duties which may be required for arctic tankers. At present the standard two-stage turbine meets the normal requirements. If, however, additional power is required for icebreaking, it may be necessary to increase the astern stages to four or six for the same 100 per cent rated ahead steam flow. This would be in the form of a cross-compound arrangement, so as to reduce gear loading at high astern torque levels. Additionally, if a single cross-compound unit were used to power a twin screw vessel, such as the "therma-coupled" arrangement, astern power on both shafts would be necessary.

With the six-stage arrangement smaller blade and wheel diameters could be employed and thus it would be possible to hold rotational losses to the level of present units.

As an alternative, G.E. (USA) are also considering an increase in the steam flow through the conventional astern unit, which would require greater flow capability from the boiler.

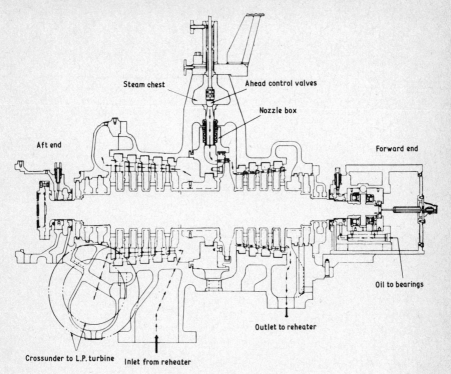

FIG. 13.—*G.E. (USA) Reheat HP-IP turbine.*

6.2.6. Blade Design and Experience

In 1960, G.E. (USA) introduced a new method for the design of blades by which all potentially dangerous vibration resonances are eliminated in the design procedure. For all turbines which have been shipped in the period from 1961 to the present day there have been no blade failures attributable to metal fatigue.

G.E. (USA) is recognized as the leader in research on blade vibration based on a careful accumulation of knowledge and experience of many years.

6.3. KAWASAKI HEAVY INDUSTRIES LIMITED (JAPAN) (K.H.I.). (With additional diagrams and information supplied by Licensees Hitachi Zozen)

The turbines built by Kawasaki are their own design and not developed from previous licence agreements. In this sense they have pursued something of an independent approach to the problems which affect all turbine design projects.

The present range which is meaningful in the context of powering modern merchant shipping is set out in Table V.

6.3.1. HP Turbine—UA Type

The sectional view in Fig. 14 of the UA frame HP turbine illustrates some interesting features. Main steam is admitted to the manoeuvring valves contained in a

TABLE V.—STEAM CYCLES OFFERED BY K.H.I. LTD

Turbine Type	UA Non Reheat	UC Non Reheat	UR Reheat	UR Reheat	UB Non Reheat	UB Non Reheat
Power range (HP)	18 000 to 36 000	36 000 to 50 000	28 000 to 31 500	40 000 to 50 000	20 000 to 25 000	40 000 to 45 000
Propeller (rev/min)	80–105	75–125	90	75–125	85	105
Steam pressure (lbs/in^2)	853	853	1420	1420	853	
Steam temperature (°C)	510–520	510–520	520		510–520	
Type of reduction gear	Double reduction tandem articulated	Double reduction locked train	Double reduction semi-locked train	Double reduction locked train	Double reduction semi-locked train	
Type of manoeuvring control	Electric-hydraulic	Electric-hydraulic	Electric-hydraulic (high pressure oil operated)	Electric-hydraulic	Electric-hydraulic (high pressure oil operated)	Electric-hydraulic
Position of propeller shaft main thrust bearing	Forward of main wheel	Forward of main wheel	Aft of main wheel	Forward of main wheel	Aft of main wheel	Aft of main wheel

Note: UA, UC & UR are standard types.
UB is not standard type i.e. 20 000 to 25 000 HP 85 rev/min and 40 000 to 45 000 HP 105 rev/min only.

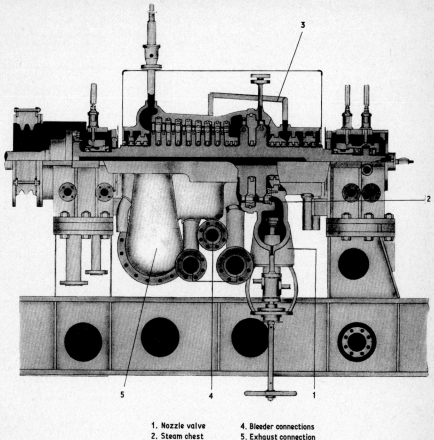

1. Nozzle valve   4. Bleeder connections
2. Steam chest   5. Exhaust connection
3. Semi–Curtis stage

FIG. 14.—*Kawasaki UA frame HP turbine.*

separate assembly forward of the HP turbine. There is no guardian valve because the movement of the ahead and astern valves are coupled together by a beam with a centrally placed fulcrum. There are other linkages connected to a hydraulically operated servo-cylinder and pilot valve, but basically it is not possible to open the astern manoeuvring valve before closing the ahead valve, and *vice versa*.

Two symmetrically arranged loop pipes supply steam from the manoeuvring valve assembly to both sides of a steam chest cast integral with the bottom-half HP turbine casing. Steam enters the main nozzle group chamber which has 28 nozzles permanently open to the manoeuvring valve. Two hand-operated valves on either side of the steam chest admit steam to two other separate nozzle group chambers, containing two nozzles each.

6.3.2. The Semi-Curtis Control Stage

The first two HP turbine expansions are of a unique patented design referred to as a semi-Curtis stage, and are used in all HP turbine frames. The manufacturers have explained that the semi-Curtis control stage has two rows of moving blades as in a conventional two-row, velocity-compounded, Curtis stage, but in the semi-Curtis arrangement the stator blades between the two rows of moving blades are a group of nozzles suitably designed not only to utilize the carry-over velocity energy from the first row of moving blades, but also to produce a further heat drop.

In other words the semi-Curtis control stage is composed of two pressure-compounded (or Rateau) stages with partial admission, as illustrated in Figure 15(a).

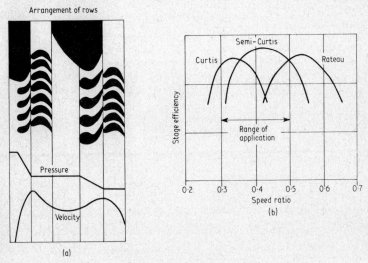

FIG. 15.—*The semi-Curtis stage, a) pressure and velocity distribution, b) comparable stage efficiencies.*

In the semi-Curtis design the heat drop across the first nozzle group is so chosen that the steam velocity at nozzle outlet is less than sonic velocity, and the heat drop across the second nozzle group is chosen to be between 33 per cent and 67 per cent of the first heat drop.

The main advantages of the semi-Curtis design are as follows:

a) Because the larger heat drop is designed to occur in the first stage, the steam pressure after the first stage nozzles is reduced sufficiently to minimize the differential pressure, and hence the leakage loss through the high pressure casing labyrinth gland seals at the inlet end. This advantage is also a feature of the two-row Curtis stage, but not for a two-stage Rateau control stage where the heat drops would usually be equally divided.

b) A two-row Curtis control stage having the same total heat-drop as a semi-Curtis two-wheel control stage would result in steam velocities at the nozzle outlet in excess of sonic velocity, and the resulting shock wave losses would reduce the control stage efficiency. Thus, the semi-Curtis control stage can be designed for a heat-drop comparable with a Curtis stage, but has a higher stage efficiency.

c) A single impulse wheel control stage can also be designed to take a large heat drop, but since the blade speed to steam velocity ratio is greater for the single impulse wheel than for the semi-Curtis control stage, a higher blade speed would be required for optimum efficiency. If the speed rotor were the same for both arrangements increased blade speed could only be obtained by increasing the impulse wheel diameter, which would result in higher disc windage and friction losses. Moreover, an increased wheel diameter would mean shorter nozzle and blade lengths if the effective flow areas were to remain constant, and this too would result in greater losses.

As shown in Figure 15(b) the semi-Curtis control stage is more efficient within a range of speed ratios from 0·35 to 0·50, than the equivalent Curtis or Rateau stages.

Another interesting feature of the HP turbine which is used on all frame sizes is the flexible coupling between HP rotor and pinion. Illustrated in Fig. 16, it will be seen that a round-ended spring-loaded centring plunger is used to maintain the male coupling teeth concentric with the female coupling teeth. There are projections in the middle of the teeth to allow free passage of the oil supply which is admitted to the outer ends of each coupling via a collecting channel through the coupling teeth to outlets on the inner faces of the coupling. A special lapping process is also employed to improve the tooth mating surfaces.

6.3.3. LP Turbine—UA, UR, and UB Types

The UA frame LP turbine is of the downward flow exhaust type. The ahead exhaust is somewhat novel in the construction of the steam deflector. The deflector is an annulus

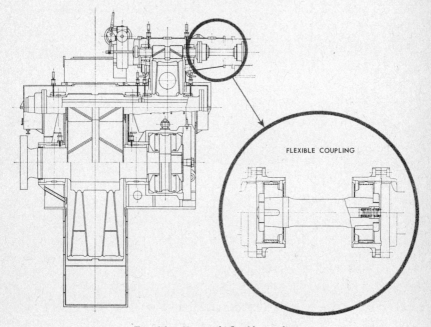

FLEXIBLE COUPLING

FIG. 16.—*Kawasaki flexible coupling.*

bolted to the inner casing exhaust at the periphery containing four circumferential guide vanes.

The UR and UB frames are of the axial-exhaust type illustrated in Fig. 17.

Points of particular interest are the astern turbine wheels which are separate shrunk-on discs, illustrated in Fig. 18.

The two Curtis wheel discs are shrunk on to bushes which are themselves keyed to the rotor. The discs are keyed to the bushes by means of a number of radial keys. The step on shaft diameter is recessed to avoid a stress concentration at the change of section and a liner collar is fitted between the recess and first disc. A circular retaining nut is fitted on the end of the assembly. It is stated by the manufacturers that concentricity of the discs under thermal stress is maintained by the short radial keys.

In Fig. 17 the first stage is a three-row velocity-compounded Curtis wheel followed by a two-row velocity-compounded stage, but in Fig. 18 both stages are two-row Curtis wheels. Astern steam is admitted at the bottom centreline.

The last three ahead stages have tapered and twisted profile blades, while only the last two stages of moving blades are fitted with stellite shields on the leading edges.

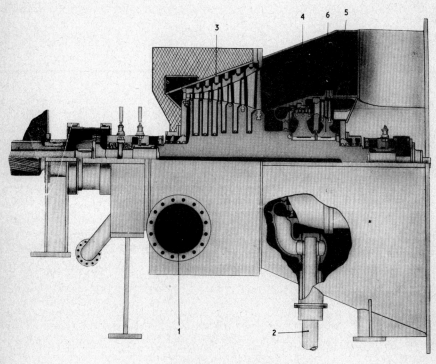

1. Ahead steam inlet	4. Astern casing
2. Astern steam inlet	5. Exhaust chamber
3. Ahead casing	6. Built up astern disc

FIG. 17.—*Kawasaki UR, UB frame LP turbine.*

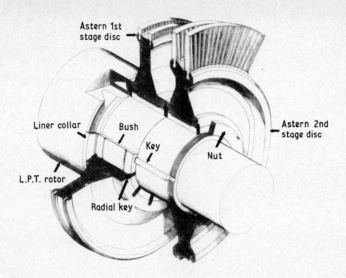

FIG. 18.—*Kawasaki. Attachment of the astern turbine discs.*

Another feature of interest is the coupling between turbine rotor and gear pinion. The coupling shaft is not the conventional short cardan shaft but more correctly a quill shaft connecting the aft end of both turbine rotor and primary pinion. Both ends are of the fine-tooth male and female type.

6.3.4. Reheat HP/IP Turbine UR Type

The Kawasaki design of reheat HP turbine is shown in Fig. 19.

Inlet steam is admitted from the manoeuvring valve assembly via a a single pipe to a nozzle chamber on the bottom half. The nozzle chamber and inlet pipe are separately cast and welded to the bottom half of the HP casing. A group of nozzles is permanently open to the main steam inlet flow of steam but a second group of nozzles contained within a separate chamber in the nozzle chamber is controlled by a single nozzle group control valve also in the bottom half.

The first control stage is the semi-Curtis type previously mentioned, followed by three impulse-reaction stages.

The reheated steam enters on the top half of the cylinder through seven further stages, leaving by an outlet on the bottom half which leads directly downwards to the cross-over pipe which loops down and away from the engine below the engine seating before returning to the LP turbine bottom half.

The same flexible coupling of the self-centring type is used as mentioned previously.

There is a flexible coupling connection on the forward end of the HP rotor to drive the main generator through a clutch and reduction gear. This system is employed on both the UB and UR types. A two-row Curtis wheel back-up turbine is used to drive the turbo-generator when the main engine-drive clutch is disengaged.

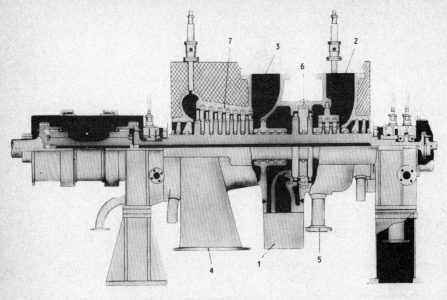

1. H.P. turbine steam inlet
2. H.P. turbine steam outlet (to reheater)
3. I.P. turbine steam inlet (from reheater)
4. I.P. turbine steam outlet

5. Bleeder connector
6. H.P. turbine
7. I.P. turbine

FIG. 19.—*Kawasaki reheat HP-IP turbine.*

Vacuum pumps are used in preference to steam air ejectors, and feed pumps are driven by separate turbines, although provision can be made to drive the feed pump from the main turbine if the owner requires it.

Lubricating oil is condensate-cooled.

6.3.5. Reheat Turbine Type UR-315—General Information

M.C.R. 30 000 shp at 90 rev/min.

Normal service 28 000 shp at 88 rev/min.

Steam conditions 1420 lbs/in^2 520°C/520°C (Reheat pressure 341 lbs/in^2).

Vacuum 722 mm Hg.

One-and-a-half boilers (main and auxiliary).

Evaporation rate 87 T/h at m.c.r. from the main boiler and 35 T/h from the auxiliary boiler.

The main generator is driven from the forward end of the main HP turbine through gearing. A hydraulically-operated clutch connects the main turbine to the generator. When disengaged, a back-up turbine drives the main generator. The arrangement is such that the back-up turbine is always turning when the main generator is turning, so some windage loss must be inevitable. There is a separate stand-by generator and an auxiliary diesel-driven generator of about one-third of the output of the other two.

The main and stand-by feed pumps are separately turbine-driven.

Lubricating oil is circulated by an electric motor-drive vertical screw pump, whilst the stand-by lubricating oil pump is turbine-driven.

In view of the high steam conditions boiler water treatment requires close attention and the use of sodium phosphate instead of the caustic soda treatment used in conventional lower-pressure boilers. Phosphate injection is controlled by continuous detection of boiler water alkalinity.

External water treatment both of feed water and make-up water includes an ion-exchanger which keeps the silica content of make-up water to less than 0·05 p.p.m. and conductivity to 1 micro-ohm per centimetre.

Oil detectors and filters with magnets are also used to keep the purity high and eliminate sludge and scale.

For manoeuvring purposes, in port, and going astern, rejeat is not required, therefore control of reheat temperature is necessary. This is done by closing the reheat dampers and opening the by-pass dampers. The Kawasaki main boiler is program-controlled, so that under normal change-over conditions the reheater temperature is changed gradually to avoid thermal shock to the turbine. It is possible to reverse the change-over in the middle of the program.

Rapid shut-down of the reheater occurs when, for example, a crash-astern is required, or when the main turbine trips out, or reheated steam pressure drops.

It is interesting to note that the manufacturers had considerable trouble with pipe flange connections and, as standard practice, have gone over to welded connections in all main steam piping from the superheater via the manoeuvring valve to the ahead and astern turbines. Welded pipe jointing is also used in the main feed discharge piping except for the feed pump outlet.

One important consideration which none of the makers of reheat turbines sems to have considered, according to the numerous drawings of turbines and piping arrangements seen by the author, is the omission of a relay-operated interceptor valve in the reheat pipe which returns to the IP section of the HP/IP combined turbine. In the event of a main propeller shaft failure or loss of propeller, the main steam supply would immediately be shut off as the overspeed trip came into operation, but with two lengths of reheat piping and reheater tubing in the boiler full of steam, the volume of steam contained in these pipes may be sufficient to increase the turbine speed beyond the rated 110 per cent or 115 per cent at which it trips because there is nothing to prevent the residual steam in the pipes from continuing through the IP and LP turbines. This would also apply in the event of failure of either the HP or LP couplings to the gearing.

The two vessels referred to by the manufacturers achieved a fuel consumption rate of 0·415 lb/hp-h and 0·413 lb/hp-h, respectively.

Apart from some preliminary difficulties the Kawasaki reheat cycle seems to have performed satisfactorily, though only two years have elapsed since they were commissioned. A longer period of operation will enable a better assessment of the overall economics and reliability of the marine reheat cycle to be undertaken. It is hoped that the manufacturers will eventually make this information known.

6.4. DE LAVAL TURBINE INCORPORATION (USA)

De Laval marine steam turbines are not featured largely among the merchant marine fleets of the world, but they have produced many units for the American Navy.

They currently hold the position of building the highest torque marine unit ever built in the world rated at 50 000 shp and 100 rev/min for installation in the 225 000 tons dwt. "Seatrain" tankers built at Brooklyn. Reports indicate that these tankers are capable of operating at $17\frac{1}{2}$ knots.

The present "3 series" range of non-reheat turbine units is illustrated in Figs. 20(a), 21(a) and 22(a), whilst the relationship between a given propeller torque and propeller rev/min given in Figs. 20(b), 21(b) and 22(b) determines the particular frame sizes of both HP and LP turbines. All three types of basic design operate at 850 lbs/in^{2}g., and 513°C with $28\frac{1}{2}$ in of mercury in the condenser.

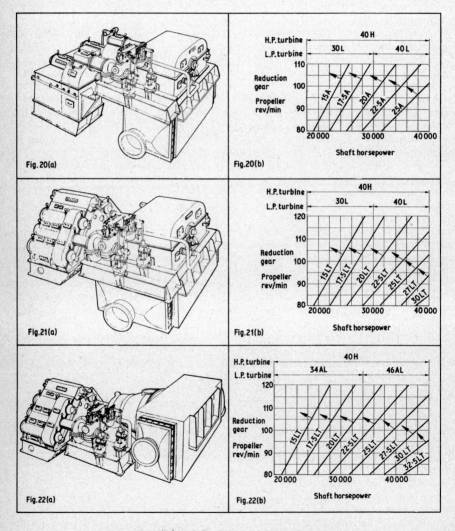

FIGS. 20, 21 AND 22.—De Laval turbine frame sizes.

The range of powers and speeds offered in Fig. 20(b) has been extended to a 65H and 65L frame size with a capability of up to 70 000 shp. It is this new frame size which is installed in the "Seatrain" tankers.

The outline of the second series of frame size illustrated in Fig. 23 gives the overall dimensions of a 32 000 shp, 103 rev/min unit employing 40 HP and 40 LP frame sizes with locked-train gearing.

Gear sizes have been developed using low speed gear diameters as a base and varying the face width to accept the required torque.

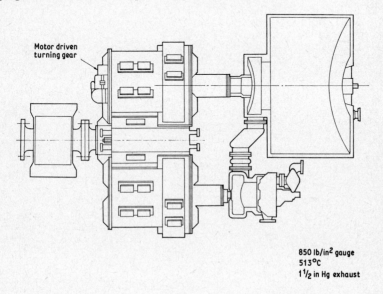

850 lb/in² gauge
513°C
1½ in Hg exhaust

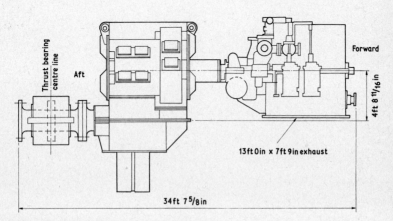

FIG. 23.—De Laval. Outline of 32 000 shp marine turbines and main reduction gear.

6.4.1. HP Turbine

The sectional elevation of the 40 H frame non-reheat turbine is shown in Fig. 24. The control valve chest is cast integral with the top half and consists of a number of groups of nozzles controlled by throttle valves which open sequentially as a common supportng valve bar is lifted. The nozzle box is cast integral with the steam chest. The diffusing chamber at the aft end has a cross-over outlet cast into the bottom half casing for easier maintenance, and the aft end is mounted solidly on the bedplate while the forward end is mounted on a flexible plate support which permits axial expansion. The thrust bearing is also at the forward end.

6.4.2. LP Turbines

The 30 L type is a downward-flow exhaust type with casing of the prefabricated type. It has nine impulse/reaction stages, the last four stages having twisted and tapered blades. The astern turbine comprises one Curtis wheel and one impulse wheel.

The axial flow exhaust LP turbine shown in Fig. 25 has a cast casing, and blading and diaphragms are very similar to the downflow exhaust LP turbine.

FIG. 24.—De Laval 40H frame HP turbine.

FIG. 25.—De Laval 30L frame LP turbine.

The astern turbine outlet faces downstream as is usual with axial flow exhaust casings, the turbine having two Curtis wheel stages.

6.4.3. Reheat Turbine

The reheat turbine shown in Fig. 26 is similar to all other designs with regard to flow path, but it is interesting to note that the first (control) stage is a Curtis wheel rather than an impulse wheel which is somewhat unusal considering the lower efficiency compared with impulse stage.

6.4.4. Lubrication System

The turbine shaft-driven positive-displacement pumps provide the over-speed signal to the governing system.

Oil supply is at 49°C and the rise is restricted to 10°C. Lubricating oil and control-actuating oil is supplied by the main lubricating oil system at full discharge pressure. Figure 27 is a diagram of the lubricating system.

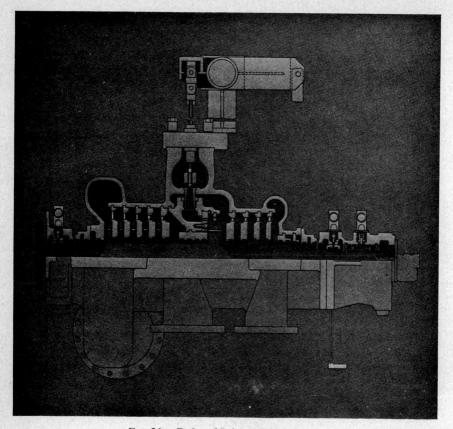

Fig. 26.—De Laval Rehat HP-LP turbine.

6.4.5. Journal Bearings

All turbine journal bearings are of the segmental tilting-pad type. This type inherently provides some sellf-alignment, but more important this bearing has been proved by experience to have great stability. Oil whirl problems are therefore eliminated.

6.4.6. Thrust Bearings

The thrust collar is forged integral with with the shaft and over-sized to provided some machining of the collar to be undertaken should a failure occur.

The six segmental thrust pads on each side are supported on levelling plates which serve to equalize the loading between pairs of pads.

6.5. GEC TURBINE GENERATORS LIMITED [G.E.C. (UK)]

The full range of marine steam turbines marketed by G.E.C. Turbine Generators Ltd. (formerly English Electric/A.E.I.), is set out in Table VI. Reheat turbines would be available when required but none has been built to date.

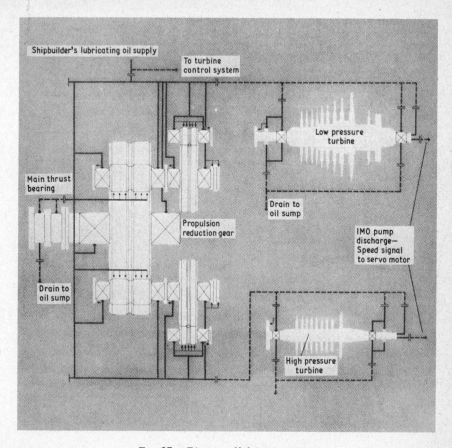

FIG. 27.—*Diagram of lubrication system.*

Details of a few of the frame sizes have been listed in Table VII. Each frame size is offered in many different combinations. Among the single cylinder turbines steam inlet conditions, power, rev/min, condenser cooling water temperature, and arrangement of condenser flows can be varied over a fairly wide range. The cross-compound turbines offer the further choice of a downward-flow or axial-flow exhaust. There is thus a wide choice of turbines for marine applications offered by the Company.

6.5.1. Single Cylinder Turbines

The main advantages of the single-cylinder propulsion turbine is the relatively low cost due to fewer moving parts, reduced complexity of gearing, pipework, etc. The width is considerably reduced compared with a cross-compound unit and, of course, it can be adapted for turbo-electric drive. The prime disadvantage is that, compared with the standard cross-compound set, the thermal efficiency is about $3\frac{1}{2}$ per cent lower.

TABLE VI.—RANGE OF G.E.C. (UK) MARINE PROPULSION GEARED TURBINE FRAMES

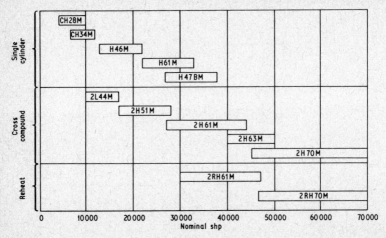

The design of such a turbine is based on acceptable compromises. In effect the centrifugal stress in the last row of moving blades determines the maximum blade diameter and speed of the rotor. To arrive at a good balance of efficiency between high and low pressure sections, some compromise has to be made in design.

Figures 28 and 29 show sections of the complete unit and the turbine respectively. The conventional Rateau staging is employed except for the astern turbine which is a Curtis stage followed by a single impulse stage.

The ahead and astern cylinders are rigidly supported from their vertical joints at the exhaust end. These vertical joints are themselves rigidly supported from two fore and aft beams on each side of the centreline. The astern cylinder is cantilevered out from the forward vertical joint while the forward bearing is carried on an extension of the lower half casing. Palm supports at the forward bearing pedestal centre line are arranged to give lateral damping and stiffness.

A separate pedestal supports the ahead casing at the aft end by palms near the horizontal joint which are keyed to the aft bearing pedestal. There is also a vertical key on the bottom half of the casing to maintain alignment yet allow axial expansion.

Gearing is of the double-helical dual-tandem articulated type, the pinions being nitrided.

6.5.2. Cross-Compound Turbine (HP Turbine)

A sectional elevation of the HP turbine is shown in Fig. 30. Since efficiency at low powers is not of particular importance in tankers and container ships, sequentially-operated manoeuvring is not used on standard designs. A single ahead manoeuvring valve supplies steam to the main group of nozzles in the bottom half-cylinder, and when required by opening one or two hand valves to smaller groups. The arrangement gives good efficiency at high powers without using more than one valve.

Bled-steam tappings can be provided at almost any stage as required. The cross-over pipe between HP and LP cylinders is a short, straight pipe incorporating a tied, balanced bellows unit to eliminate pressure thrusts.

TABLE VII.—G.E.C. (UK) MARINE PROPULSION GEARED TURBINES

		Cross-compound		Single Cylinder		Reheat
	Frame	2H61M	2H70M	CH34M	H61M	2RH70M
Turbine—						
Steam conditions at T.S.V. (Max.)		900 lbs/in²g 950°F	900 lbs/in²g 950°F	900 lbs/in²g 950°F	900 lbs/in²g 950°F	1400 lbs/in²g 950/950°F
Vacuum at service power (Nominal)		28·5" Hg in 75°F seas	28·5" Hg in 75°F seas	28·5" Hg in 75°F seas	28·5" Hg in 75°F seas	28·5" Hg in 75°F seas
Maximum economic power range		28 000 to 45 000 shp	40 000 to 70 000 shp	7000 to 13 500 shp	20 000 to 30 000 shp	47 000 to 70 000 shp
Maximum astern power		50 per cent ahead power	50 per cent ahead power	c.p. propeller	50 per cent ahead power	50 per cent ahead power
Nominal power division	HP turbine/LP turbine	50 per cent–50 per cent	50 per cent–50 per cent	single cylinder	single cylinder	50 per cent–50 per cent
Maximum rotor speed	HP turbine / LP turbine	6500 rev/min / 3500 rev/min	5000 rev/min / 3000 rev/min	6300 rev/min	5000 rev/min	5000 rev/min / 3000 rev/min
Staging	HP turbine	single row control +7 impulse stages	single row control +7 impulse stages	single row control +8 impulse stages +3 reaction stages *or* 2 row control +7 impulse +3 reaction	single row control +10 impulse stages +4 reaction stages	single row control +4 impulse stages +4 impulse stages
Staging	LP turbine	4 impulse stages +3 reaction stages	3 impulse stages +3 reaction stages			5 impulse stages +3 reaction stages
Staging	Astern turbine	2 row Curtis +2 impulse stages	2 row Curtis +2 impulse stages	none	2 row Curtis +1 impulse stages	2 row Curtis +2 impulse stages
Lubricating oil	Requirements (turbine only)	105 g.p.m.		30 g.p.m.		
	Pressure	10–15 lbs/in²g	10–15 lbs/in²g	10–15 lbs/in²g	10–15 lbs/in²g	10–15 lbs/in²g

NOTE.—All stages other than 2 row control stages (Curtis) in fact use impulse-reaction blading. In above table the term "reaction" means stages with cast diaphragms and twisted runner blades.

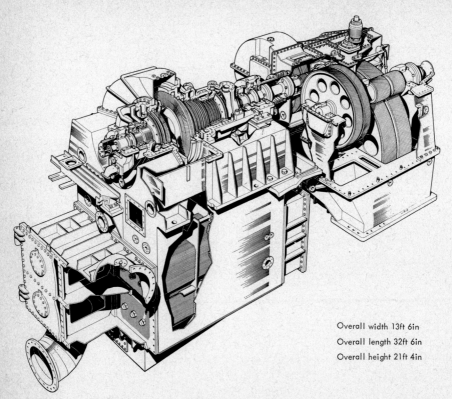

Overall width 13ft 6in
Overall length 32ft 6in
Overall height 21ft 4in

FIG. 28.—*G.E.C. (UK) single-cylinder turbine. Overall width 13 ft 6 in, overall length 32 ft 6 in, overall height 21 ft 4 in.*

All other pipe connections are located in the bottom half to facilitate lifting the top half-casing.

6.5.3. Thrust Bearing

Thrust bearings on all the manufacturer's rotors are of the tilting pad type with oil outlet at the top and separate thrust collars with case-hardened faces, which are retained on the rotor by means of an interference fit, a longitudinal key and a circumferential retaining-ring.

6.5.4. Control Gear

The manoeuvring valves are contained in a separate steam chest mounted so as to resist forces and moments imposed by the main steam piping.

Valves are hydraulically operated at 150 lbs/in^2 oil pressure supplied by a positive-displacement pump, driven by an electric motor. There is a standby pump, also electrically-driven.

The manoeuvring valve control gear has a cam-operated feedback, giving an almost linear relationship between controller and propeller speed.

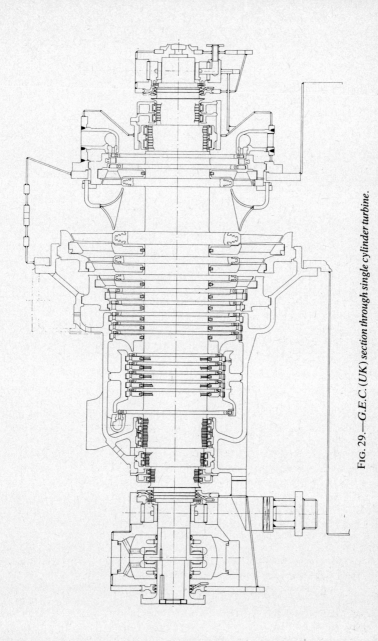

FIG. 29.—G.E.C. (UK) section through single cylinder turbine.

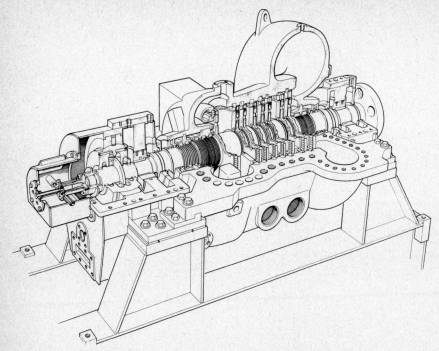

FIG. 30.—*G.E.C. (UK) sectional arrangement of HP (2H61 frame)*.

The ahead manoeuvring valve can be provided with a speed sensitive control which can be set to operate at any speed between 70 per cent and 100 per cent. For this purpose a governor can be fitted on the forward end of the HP rotor, as illustrated in Fig. 31, to provide a speed sensitive oil pressure signal to operate the ahead manoeuvring valve. It consists of a balanced cantilever leak-off valve with a supply orifice and viscosity compensating system to give consistent speed/pressure settings.

An overspeed trip set for 115 per cent of the rated speed drains the oil closing the ahead manoeuvring valve but steam can still be supplied to the astern turbine.

The overspeed trip unit consists of an electrical impulse inductive sensing-head, operating a trip valve through an amplifier. Means are provided to depress the tripping speed so as to enable the device to be tested at normal speed.

6.5.5. LP Turbine–Downward Exhaust Path

The LP casing of prefabricated construction, Fig. 32, the first four diaphragms being of welded construction whereas the larger fixed blades at the exhaust end are cast into high quality cast iron. Special drainage belts are provided in the wet steam region of the ahead turbine with shaped dams behind drainage holes to collect water and lead it to the condenser.

The astern turbine nozzle box inlet and belt are located in the bottom half-casing.

The aft support feet are free to move laterally and the forward feet may move both laterally and fore-and-aft to accommodate thermal expansion, while keys at the bottom

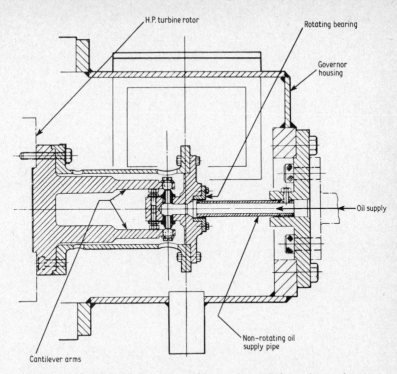

FIG. 31.—*G.E.C. (UK) Governor used for speed control of propulsion turbines.*

of both the forward and aft bearing pedestals maintain the athwartships position. A general arrangement of this unit is shown in Fig. 33.

6.5.6. LP Turbine–Axial Exhaust Path

A sectional elevation is shown in Fig. 34 and a general arrangement is shown in Fig. 35. The inherent advantages of the condenser mounted independently of the LP turbine can be fully exploited by careful design of the turbine to condenser exhaust arrangement and cylinder fabrication. Wing ducts taking the exhaust steam to the condenser are arranged to give complete access to the forward LP journal bearing and this in turn allows the forward and aft bearing pedestals to be virtually centreline-mounted in recesses machined into substantial palm supports, built out from the ahead and astern cylinders. The ship's seatings extend directly up to the cylinder palms which give maximum support rigidity as near as possible to the turbine rotor centreline. This minimizes alignment changes when the structural temperature of the cylinder fluctuates, such as when manoeuvring.

The cylinder fabrication is designed so that extraction bleed points can be selected from all ahead stages after stage 1, and the resulting box structure is extremely rigid and symmetrical. To provide stiffness at the exhaust openings the casing is stiffened by tubular struts and these are carefully positioned to avoid resonance that may affect the last row blading and to minimize transfer losses.

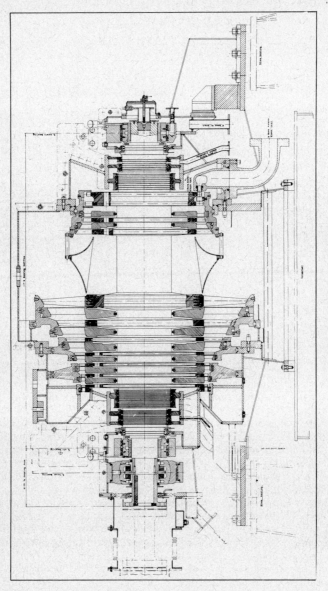

FIG. 32.—*G.E.C. (UK) LP turbine.*

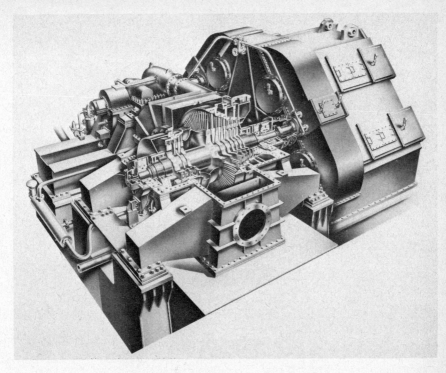

FIG. 33.—*G.E.C. (UK) cross-compounded HP-LP turbine and double reduction gearing (down-flow exhaust).*

The ducts are designed to accept the large forces exerted by vacuum loading. They are constructed in one piece and the strength of the duct enables the anchor points of the condenser and LP cylinder assembly to be located at the ship's seating, shared by the aft end of the condenser and LP forward bearing pedestal. Thus, the thermal expansion of the condenser and LP turbine are prevented from becoming additive and problems associated with excessive axial movement of the coupling are avoided.

6.5.7. Bauman Multi-Exhaust

A feature of particular interest which could be employed in single-cylinder or cross-compound LP turbine exhausts can be seen in Fig. 36. The flow of steam passing the penultimate LP stage is split into two flows by a circular ring on the nozzle. The outer flow at the tip is delivered directly into the condenser space whilst the inner flow is continued through the last stage blading and out to the condenser space. The volume of steam flowing into the final stage is therefore less and the final stage blade-length can be reduced. Since as previously mentioned, in the case of single cylinder turbines the exhaust area is determined by the maximum centrifugal stress of the last stage blades, by shortening the last stage blade, higher rotational speeds can be employed, enabling a higher power to be developed.

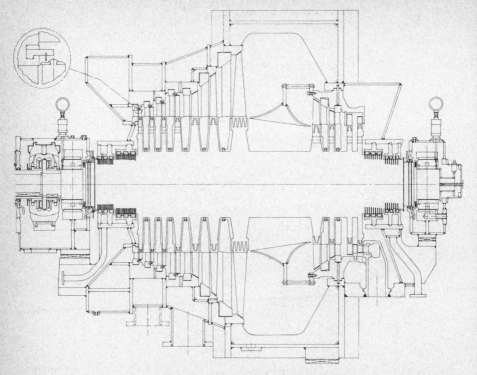

FIG. 34.—*G.E.C. (UK) sectional arrangement of LP turbine.*

The split-flow moving blade is of a special shape and it has been claimed that with three additional rows of blades the power may be increased four times for the same speed and factor of safety. Normally, however, only one split flow is used.

The special shape of the penultimate moving blade and the special diaphragms would, of course, increase the cost of such a turbine, but the gain in power may overcome that disadvantage. It is possible that the single cylinder turbines in the 20 000 to 38 000 shp range may be designed on this principle.

6.6. BLOHM & VOSS (WEST GERMANY)

6.6.1. HP Turbine

The most outstanding feature of the B. & V. propulsion unit is the unconventional HP turbine which is a 50 per cent reaction type, often referred to as a "Parsons" turbine or simply "reaction" type turbine. It is a 26-stage unit employing throttle-valve control with full 360° inlet steam admission area.

It will be seen in Fig. 37 that the construction of the rotor is the solid drum type with the fixed blades on two separate cylindrical carriers which are spigotted circumferentially into the outer casing, supported at the horizontal joint and dowelled top and bottom. The circumferential spigots act as partitions between the inlet, bled steam, and outlet spaces. The inner cylinders have bolted horizontal joints as shown in a view of the bottom casing in Fig. 38.

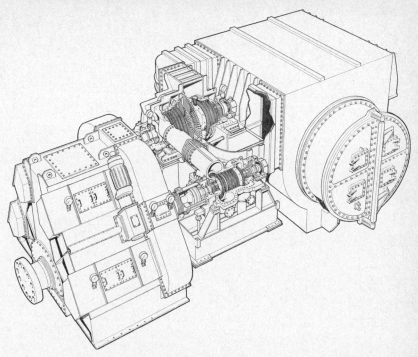

FIG. 35.—*G.E.C. (UK) cross-compounded HP-LP turbine and double reduction gearbox with single-plane axial-flow exhaust.*

As with all designs of 50 per cent reaction turbines, a dummy piston is necessary to balance the axial force on the rotor due to expansion of the steam through the moving blades. The dummy piston can be seen at the steam inlet end of the rotor in Fig. 37.

The outer casing and inner casings are designed to be symmetrical top and bottom at each section.

Steam enters top and bottom and exhausts top and bottom, while the cross section illustrates the smooth transition from shell thickness to flange.

The casing design is intended to reduce unequal heating and minimize inner and outer casing thermal distortion, for whilst 50 per cent reaction blades are less affected by friction losses than impulse blades, leakage losses over the blade tips have a marked effect upon the efficiency of reaction turbines. The working clearances between blade tip and casing and tip and rotor have of necessity to be small. Thus the circularity of the inner casing must be maintained under all transient operating conditions.

The manufacturers claim that symmetrically arranged inlet and outlet pipes reduce forces and moments on the casing. By halving the cross-section of the pipes, diameters and wall thicknesses are reduced and section modulli are correspondingly smaller, which is an important factor in relatively short pipes.

Outer casing horizontal joint bolts have the usual central holes for heating rods which achieve accurate pre-tensioning. Expansion sleeves ensure that bolts will not be stretched excessively when steam is first applied to the turbine.

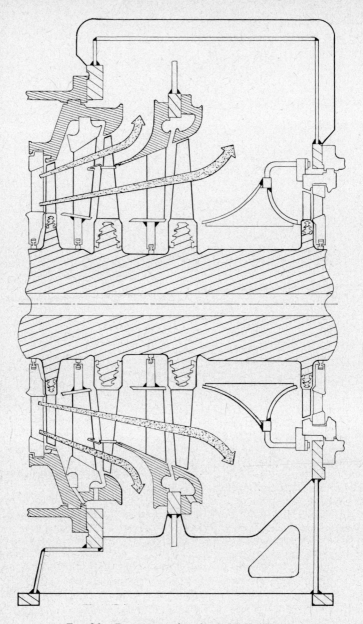

FIG. 36.—*Baumann multi-exhaust (G.E.C.(UK))*.

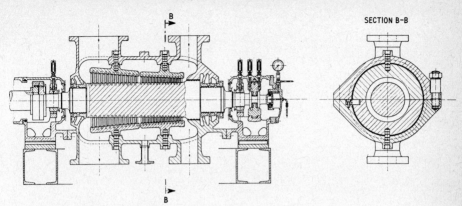

FIG. 37.—*Blohm and Voss sectional views through the HP turbine.*

The outer casing is bolted fore and aft to the two main bearing pedestals by means of half-ring flanges cast integral with the bottom half.

The turbine is mounted on an anti-torsion bedplate with seatings for the two bearing pedestals. The forward pedestal is fixed rigidly to the forward bedplate seating, while the aft pedestal is mounted on a panting plate type support to permit thermal expansion of the casing aftwards. The double-collar thrust bearing is located at the forward end.

It has been stated that the critical speed of the HP rotor is at least 25 per cent above the maximum operating speed, and this has been claimed to eliminate the possibility of vibration within the operating speed range. However, although the author would agree that the large solid rotor employed may never exhibit the characteristics associated with operation at the critical speed, he would point out that the quoted figure probably refers to the critical speed calculated on the basis of the assumption of rigid bearing supports. The actual critical speed of the rotor will probably lie within the operating speed range due to oil film and bearing support flexibility.

A novel feature of the HP reaction blade tips is shown in Fig. 39. The moving and fixed blades at each stage are identical and rely on close tolerances between tip and surface to reduce leakage over the tips. Some years ago 50 per cent reaction blade manufacture was completed with machining of the tips to produce a fine rubbing edge which destroyed both the concave and convex profile at the tip. The diagram illustrates that Blohm & Voss in their earlier designs milled the concave side of the profile. Their present design, however, employs spark-machining of the tip which hollows out the blade tip leaving the profile unaffected. This has led to an improvement in stage efficiency, and as illustrated acts in the same way as a gland seal arrangement with two steam throttling fins.

The manufacturer's claim, with the aid of the H–Ø diagram in Fig. 40, to show the higher efficiency of the throttle-controlled reaction turbine at full load, and the reduced efficiency of the throttle controlled reaction turbine at 50 per cent load, both of which are compared with the nozzle-group controlled impulse turbine. Of course, the comparison is dependent on many factors such as the type of turbine using nozzle-group control, the steam cycle arrangement, blade and nozzle design, and the numbers of nozzles in each group, etc.

FIG. 38.—*Blohm and Voss HP-turbine dismantled.*

Blade-tip thinned on one side by machining

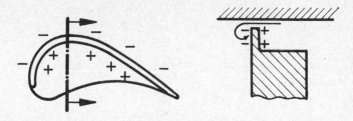

Blade-tip thinned by elytrolytic treatment

FIG. 39.—*Blohm and Voss tip-thinning on fixed and moving blades.*

P_i and t_i are the steam inlet conditions, while P_0 and t_0 are the pressure and temperature behind the fully open controlling valves. At 100 per cent power the throttle-controlled reaction turbine enthalpy is greater than the nozzle-group type, where P_r and t_r represent the steam conditions in the nozzle-group wheel chamber, P_k being the common condenser pressure.

It is a well known fact that an impulse stage is less efficient than a reaction stage, but the heat-drop in the impulse stage is much larger than the heat-drop in a single reaction stage, and thus a reaction turbine requires many more stages to complete the same expansion. It is because the heat-drop in the impulse wheel is so large (from P_i, t_i, to P_r, t_r) that the two expansion curves are so far displaced from one another at 100 per cent power.

The 50 per cent power curve illustrates that the reaction turbine is less efficient because the throttled steam at P'_E and t'_E results in a smaller total heat-drop to the common condenser pressure P'_k. The curve of 50 per cent power for the impulse wheel turbine illustrates that the first stage does most of the work at reduced powers less efficiently.

The first marine propulsion turbine of this series with throttle control was delivered in December 1970, designed for a maximum continuous rating (m.c.r.) of 16 250 shp (metric), the steam inlet conditions being 42 ata, 500°C, and condenser pressure of 0·52 ata. The HP turbine rotor speed was 7000 rev/min, the LP rotor speed 4500 rev/min reduced through MAAG locked-train type gears to a propeller speed of

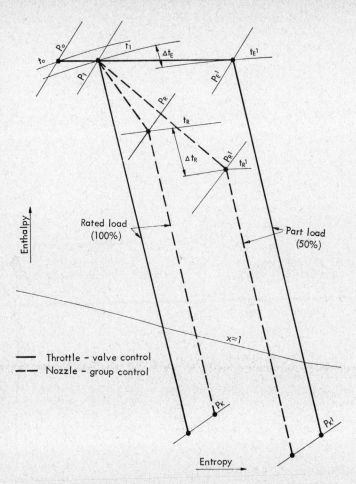

FIG. 40.—*H-Ø diagram showing expansion lines (Blohm and Voss).*

120 rev/min. The small diameter of the HP rotor and relatively high rotor speed are necessary because the optimum stage efficiency of a 50 per cent reaction turbine is achieved at higher velocity ratios than a comparable impulse type.

6.6.2. LP Turbine

The LP turbine is conventional in most respects with the majority of other manufacturers of LP turbines. The ahead blades are mounted on wheels of the same diameter, therefore in broad terms as the blade lengths increase the percentage of reaction increases proportionally. The manufacturers state that the percentage of reaction at the mean blade section of stage 1 is about +20 per cent increasing to about +45 per cent at the last stage.

Had the concept of 50 per cent reaction stages in the LP turbine been employed here the rotor would have to be extremely long, and in consequence the overall length of the unit would be prohibitive if the axial-exhaust and combined astern wheel were employed. The problem could be overcome with a double flow (split-flow) LP rotor, but this would probably necessitate a downward flow exhaust, and the overall height of the unit could be prohibitive.

The astern turbine down-stream of the ahead turbine exhausts axially in the same direction as the ahead turbine, which is one of the conventional arrangements of modern turbines which also prevents heating of the ahead turbine when the astern turbine is operating. There are two velocity-compounded stages in the astern turbine.

The LP casing and the astern inner casing are obviously cast rather than prefabricated and the principle of symmetry of the casing is employed here also. The exhaust end (forward) is fixed and the casing, which is bolted to the bearing pedestal in the same way as the HP turbine, is allowed to expand aft. Access to the forward bearing is through a well in the LP casing. The arrangement is shown clearly in Fig 41, whilst the overall dimensions are shown in Fig. 42.

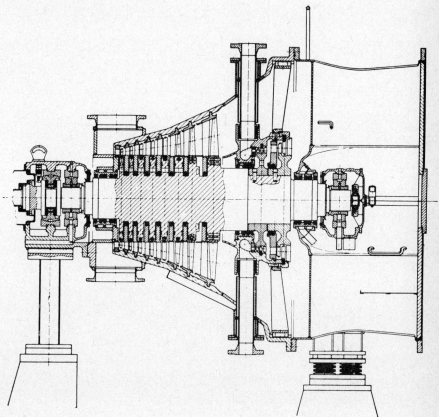

FIG. 41.—*Blohm and Voss sectional drawing of the LP-turbine.*

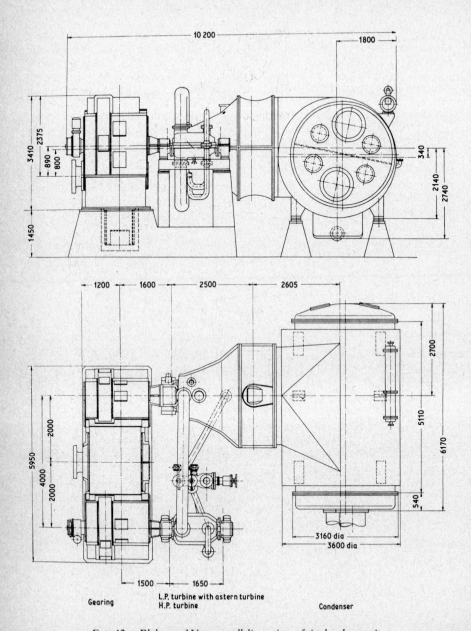

Gearing

L.P. turbine with astern turbine
H.P. turbine

Condenser

FIG. 42.—*Blohm and Voss overall dimensions of single-plane unit.*

FIG. 43.—*Blohm and Voss mounting of LP rotor.*

A view of an LP rotor being lowered into the bottom half casing can be seen in Fig. 43. It will be seen that the last three ahead rows of blades are tapered and twisted and do not have shrouding. Lacing wires are fitted to inhibit certain modes of vibration.

Table VIII sets out the various combinations of HP and LP turbines for a given maximum power.

TABLE VIII.—BLOHM & VOSS TURBINE FRAME SIZES

Type	HP Turbine	LP Turbine	Max. Power [PS]
PT 20		PTN 20	23 000
PT 25	PTH 32	PTN 25	28 000
PT 32		PTN 32	35 000
PT 40	PTH 50	PTN 40	45 000
PT 50		PTN 50	55 000

The manufacturers state that they are presently employed on developing reheat steam turbine units up to about 60 000 shp.

The manoeuvring valve and control diagram is not included but these are quite conventional, employing an oil impeller on the forward end of the LP shaft to hydraulically control the speed of the unit. An oil impeller is also installed on the HP shaft forward end which can be used in emergency. There are the usual other safety devices installed.

7. A REVIEW OF THE IMMEDIATE FUTURE

(Shipping Statistics Taken on 1st February 1974)

It is worth examining the market for steam turbines in the immediate future so that some idea of the numbers and powers required can be seen. It is not intended to present arguments in favour or against the motor or turbine for main propulsion of vessels but merely to illustrate the present requirements and the likely numbers of steam turbines which will be needed. Leaving aside vessels like passenger ships and general cargo ships on the grounds that there are insufficient of the former built to make much impact on turbine manufacturers, and the latter on the grounds that both size and tradition make the use of steam turbines unlikely, five other types of vessel were examined:

a) The Oil Tanker.
b) The Container ship.
c) The Ore, Bulk and Ore/Oil Carrier.
d) The Liquefied Gas Carrier.
e) The Chemicals Tanker.

Up to July 1971, when the statistics were first examined, chemicals tankers could be ruled out as offering a suitable market for steam turbines. Of the 225 vessels considered, the largest was 37 625 tons deadweight with a steam turbine delivering 16 000 shp at $17\frac{1}{2}$ knots. The majority was of the 400 to 7 000 tons deadweight size, and only five of the 225 were steam turbine-powered. In February 1974 this situation had not changed significantly.

Figures 44, 45, 46 and 47 illustrate the total number of steam turbine-powered vessels built and on order each year with accompanying curves of the average shp per screw for each vessel.

7.1. TYPES OF MERCHANT VESSELS POWERED BY STEAM TURBINES

7.7.1. Tankers

It can be seen from Fig. 44 that the number of oil tankers over 80 000 tons deadweight on order at the end of 1974 was almost double the number built at the beginning of that year. However, most of the orders were probably placed during the boom period, just before the oil crisis at the end of 1973.

Many of these orders have subsequently been cancelled or deferred, therefore at any instant of time after 1st February 1974 when the statistical information was obtained, the picture could be rather different.

During the boom period when shipyard order books were full it was necessary to place an order many years in advance of completion dates. It seems likely, therefore,

63

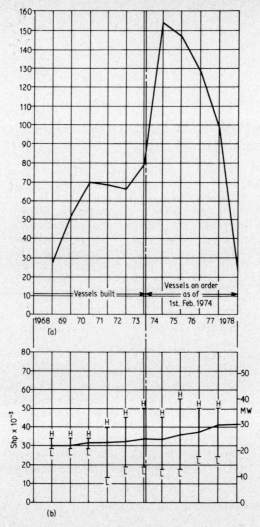

FIG. 44.—*Oil tankers (over 80 000 dwt). (a) Total number of vessels with steam turbines built or on order per year. (b) Average total power per screw per vessel (with highest and lowest powers per screw per year).*

that the effects of the oil crisis on numbers of tankers completed may not begin to be apparent before the end of 1976 or later.

For the immediate future the number of steam turbine propulsion units required per annum will probably be the same as or slightly in excess of the average of the three previous years, (i.e. about 70 to 80 per annum). The service speed of tankers will probably continue to be limited to between 15 and 17 knots for some years ahead therefore the average power requirements will continue to rise slowly.

7.1.2. Container Ships

The average shp requirements per screw for container ships appears to be levelling off at about 35 000 shp, as seen from Fig. 45, and the number on order as of 1st February 1974 have decreased sharply. Nevertheless, this is a market for the most highly rated steam turbines afloat. The Sea-Land SL-7 container ships now in service have ratings of up to 60 000 shp per screw. They are twin screw vessels of 43 400 dwt, capable of 33 knots. About 50 per cent of the container ships built since 1970 are twin-screw. One 21 300 tons dwt vessel is powered by a steam turbine delivering 50 000 shp on a single screw, with a service speed of 25 knots.

Surprisingly there were 227 container ships in operation at the last survey in 1971. Some 60 or more converted by the Americans from oil tankers, cargo vessels and naval craft operate at 13 to 16 knots and are steam turbine-powered. In fact the number of

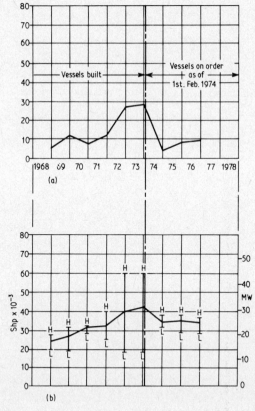

FIG. 45.—*Containerships. (a) Total number of vessels with steam turbines built or on order per year. (b) Average total power per screw per vessel (with highest and lowest powers per screw per year).*

container ships now in service may be too many for the market, hence the relatively small number built since 1968.

The conventional container ship market may well be affected by the new concepts of LASH and SEABEE ships. (LASH—lighter aboard ship; SEABEE—sea barge.) There are some 13 LASH vessels with steam turbine propulsion in service, which are of De Laval manufacture developing 32 000 shp on a single screw, and 3 SEABEE vessels with G.E. (USA) 35 000 shp steam turbines.

7.1.3. Ore, Bulk, Ore/Oil Carriers and Liquefied Gas Carriers

Ore, bulk, ore/oil carriers (OBO's) and liquefied gas carriers, Figs. 46 and 47, have not presented a large market for steam turbines, but average power requirements show an upward trend as sizes of vessels are increased each year. Therefore it may be reasoned that the numbers powered with steam turbines could increase as deadweights increase.

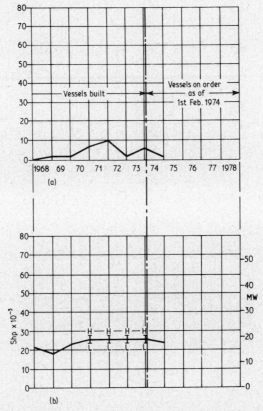

FIG. 46.—*Ore/bulk/oil carriers. (a) Total number of vessels with steam turbines built or on order per year. (b) Average total power per screw per vessel (with highest and lowest power per screw per year).*

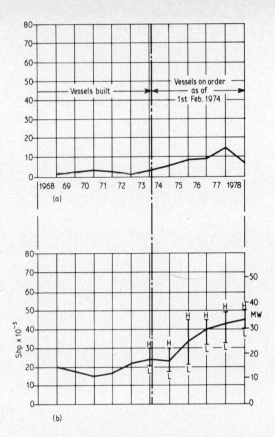

FIG. 47.—*Liquified gas carriers. (a) Total number of vessels with steam turbines built or on order per year. (b) Average total power per screw per vessel (with highest and lowest powers per screw per year).*

Like oil tankers, average speeds are 15 to 17 knots, so the power requirements would be roughly in line with increasing size, and steam turbines may be preferred for propulsion as deadweights increase to the equivalent VLCC size.

There is some evidence that liquefied gas carriers may require higher powers because service speeds are tending to increase.

For the immediate future, however, these vessels do not provide a real market for steam turbines.

7.2. CHANGES IN TRADING PATTERN

Figure 48—the total number of tankers in the world 1st January, 1971, illustrates the decline in numbers of tankers of 60 000 to 150 000 tons deadweight following the Suez Canal closure in 1967. Although the VLCC (very large crude oil carrier) was

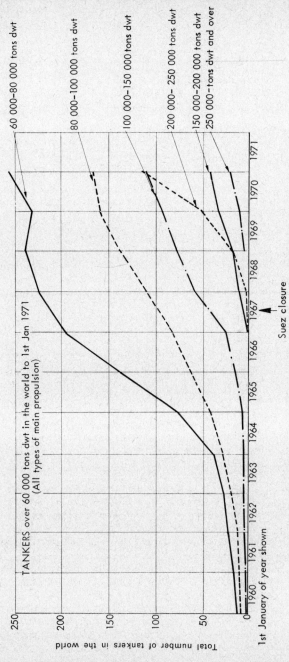

FIG. 48.—*Tankers over 60 000 dwt in the world to 18 January 1971 (all types of main propulsion).*

initiated before the Suez closure, vessels of up to 200 000 tons dwt. could only pass through the Canal in the ballast condition. The Suez closure therefore provided the required impetus for wholesale ordering which followed, and the subsequent increase in size beyond 200 000 tons dwt. This is an example of geographical influences on the shipping markets.

After the oil crisis in 1973 and the subsequent large increase in the cost of crude oil all the consumer countries were forced to restrict their demand and tanker charter rates fell dramatically. This led to newly-completed tankers being laid up, delivery dates deferred and cancellation of new building orders. This may be considered to be an ecological influence on shipping, conserving natural resources.

There could also be some changes in market trends with the development of a larger European Economic Community and the opening of a new market with countries like Communist China.

7.3. MANUFACTURERS

Table IX was compiled from statistics obtained from Fairplay International Shipping Journal, No. 38, and illustrates the distribution of turbines ordered for newbuilding vessels up to the end of 1978, showing the numbers of a particular design chosen as of 1st February 1974. Many of the types will be manufactured under licence agreements with enginebuilders outside the country of origin.

This raises an important point in connection with future trends, for some shipbuilders are offering a standard hull design for tankers, for example, and incorporating a particular make of main steam turbine for which their enginebuilders are the licencees. If this trend spreads to other yards, the market for particular makes of turbine may be determined to a large extent by the present licence agreements.

Table IX illustrates clearly that turbines designed by Messrs. Stal-Laval have the largest share of the marine steam turbine market to date with G.E. (USA) of America following. The Japanese manufacturers are individually highly placed, and collectively with 208 have the largest share. Collectively the American manufacturers have a lower figure of 137 turbines on order.

It is probably significant that Stal-Laval has licence agreements with 18 enginebuilders in Britain, France, Italy, Germany and Japan which is probably the largest number of licence agreements for any one make of turbine. Two of the 18 are sub-licencees and eleven are active turbine manufacturers. Similarly General Electric Company (USA) has world-wide manufacturing associates located in Norway, the Netherlands, Italy, Germany, France and Spain. These associates manufacture and assemble General Electric-designed ship propulsion turbines and gears.

Only a company with adequate back-up market, and technical research facilities can survive in this field. Many of the large manufacturers also build land turbine sets and thereby have the benefit of accumulated experience to contribute to the marine side, or supply turbo-generators for marine use as a diversification of products. Other manufacturers have large contracts to supply turbine machinery for naval vessels. In this country with the untimely demise of *Pametrada* at Wallsend only one combine exists for the design and manufacture of marine steam turbines, and since naval surface vessels in the UK defence system have gone over to gas turbine propulsion machinery, British-designed marine steam turbines may soon be in the minority or worse, unless the upswing to turbine machinery can be improved and the British-designed steam turbine produced competitively for the foreign market.

TABLE IX.—NEW CONSTRUCTION SHIPS UP TO 1978—WORLD DISTRIBUTION OF ORDERS FOR STEAM TURBINES

Design Type	K.H.I.						M.H.I.						I.H.I.						Stal-Laval					
Year of Completion	74	75	76	77	78	Not known	74	75	76	77	78	Not known	74	75	76	77	78	Not known	74	75	76	77	78	Not known
Oil tankers over 150 000 dwt.	22	14	16	9	2	1	21	28	11	7	—	3	18	17	20	11	—	2	42	34	28	22	2	1
Oil tankers under 150 000 dwt.																			—	1	2	3	—	—
Containerships																								
Ore/Bulk/Oil and Ore/Oil Carriers							2											1	4					
LNG Carriers				2	1														1	6	2	3		
Products tankers																								
Bulk carriers																								
Dry cargo																								
Yearly totals	22	14	16	11	3	1	23	28	11	7	—	3	18	17	20	11	—	3	47	41	32	28	2	1
Manufacturer's Totals	67						72						69						151					

Design Type	Blohm & Voss						A.E.G.						G.E. (USA)						De Laval					
Year of Completion	74	75	76	77	78	Not known	74	75	76	77	78	Not known	74	75	76	77	78	Not known	74	75	76	77	78	Not known
Oil tankers over 150 000 dwt.	—	—	—	—	—	—	4	3	2	1	—	—	12	13	19	13	6	2	4	4	—	—	—	—
Oil tankers under 150 000 dwt.							2	3	2	—	—	—	4	2	3	4	2	—						
Containerships													1	8	9	—	—	—	1	—	—	—	1	1
Ore/Bulk/Oil and Ore/Oil Carriers						—							1	—	—	—	—	1						
LNG Carriers	2	—	—	—	—	—							1	1	3	1	—	—						
Products tankers													—	1	1	1	—	—						
Bulk carriers													—	2	—	—	—	—						
Dry cargo													—	1	—	—	—	2	5	1	—	—	—	2
Yearly Totals	2	—	—	—	—	—	6	6	4	1	—	—	19	28	35	19	8	5	10	5	—	—	—	3
Manufacturer's Totals	2						17						114						18					

Design Type / Year of Completion	Westinghouse						G.E.C. (UK)						Manufacturer not indicated						Total number of turbines in each vessel type
	74	75	76	77	78	Not known	74	75	76	77	78	Not known	74	75	76	77	78	Not known	
Oil tankers over 150 000 dwt.	—	—	—	—	—	—	1	2	2	1	—	—	16	27	24	26	12	5	530
Oil tankers under 150 000 dwt.					—								1	1	—	—	—	3	33
Containerships	1					1													22
Ore/Bulk/Oil and Ore/Oil Carriers															1		—	5	15
LNG Carriers													—	1	4	11	9	1	49
Products tankers																			3
Bulk carriers					—	3													5
Dry cargo																			11
Yearly totals	1					4	1	2	2	1	—	—	17	29	29	37	21	14	668
Manufacturer's Totals	5						6						147						

Note: Analysis of world ships on order at 1st February, 1974, taken from Fairplay International Shipping Journal No. 38, February, 1974.
Comments: Stal-Laval have the largest share with 36 per cent of the order placed with turbine manufacturers. General Electric Company (USA) have the second largest share of 27 per cent of the orders placed with turbine manufacturers. Although there are still some 147 turbine sets for which the design type has not been specified it is apparent that G.E. (USA) have orders for turbines over a wider range of vessel types than Stal-Laval.

7.4. NUCLEAR PROPULSION FOR TANKERS

Whilst nuclear reactor steam-raising plant and wet steam cycle turbines are a demonstrably feasible proposition, both in naval and merchant shipping, capital costs are still too high to be attractive to the independent tanker owners who own 80 per cent of the world tanker tonnage (1974). The Royal Navy still has a requirement for steam turbine main propulsion units for nuclear submarines, and these are designed and manufactured by G.E.C. Turbine Generators Ltd.

Further, it will take many years to convince pollution conscious public and private sectors that nuclear reactors will be inherently safe in operation, collision, or total loss. The likelihood of nuclear propulsion of VLCC therefore seems most remote when viewed in terms of pollution hazards alone.

In the long term there seems to be little doubt that some alternative to oil or coal fuel will be necessary, but by then oil tankers will be virtually extinct. At present, however, the steam turbine remains the most effective means of converting nuclear energy into mechanical power and would therefore be the automatic choice if merchant fleets were to change to nuclear fuel.

7.5. GAS TURBINES

Economic studies undertaken in America have concluded that the steam propulsion plant will be the preferred propulsion installation. However, comparisons are extremely difficult to make without the benefit of adequate experience in operating gas turbine installations in merchant shipping.

The Euro-freighter concept is pioneering the "marinized" aero-engine gas turbine power plant of 30 000 shp on each of twin screws, and may provide some very interesting data in due course.

The great advantage of the steam plant is still the fact that it can burn low quality residual fuels, whereas the gas turbine requires elaborate fuel oil treatment, adding to the already high cost of fuel oil. There is also the problem of operation in a salt-laden air environment which could build up deposits on the moving and fixed blades, unless some form of filtration of intake air is employed.

7.6. FUTURE PROSPECTS

Without doubt the most significant single factor in the early 1970s which affected the economic and trading position of the industrial nations of the world was the oil crsis in late 1973, and the subsequent increase in the cost of crude oil. Literally overnight came the realization that this (and many other resources) were not only limited, but could be withheld for political or economic gain. Whilst it is still too early to predict the course of events in the long term, the immediate effects have been a turn-down in crude oil consumption leading to the laying-up of VLCC, cancelled orders, deferred delivery dates and something of a recession in most industrial countries.

It seems likely that such conditions will continue during a period of re-adjustment by both the producing and consuming nations; but, in the meantime the emphasis will be on economizing and finding alternative sources of crude oil and other fuels. There will almost certainly be a surplus of tankers for the transportation of crude oil up to the later part of the '70s, but as the search for other sources of oil and alternative fuels begins to take effect there could be a fall in the price of oil from over production in a world coming to terms with reduced growth rate.

Whether this would again lead to a boom in the tanker industry as suggested by some experts is questionable, but it is hardly likely to be on the scale of the 1973 boom.

If, as seems likely, the nations of the world continue to expand their industrial economy, albeit at a comparatively reduced rate, the demand for oil should remain high, for oil has so many advantages as a fuel, that consumers will be reluctant to exchange it for something else, providing that the price is right. If oil remains popular there is little chance of the VLCC disappearing from the seas for some time to come, and the advantages of a slow-revolution propeller make the geared marine steam turbine the most suitable propulsion unit for such vessels. There may well be a reduction in the number of types of designs of steam turbine currently available, and a greater emphasis will be placed upon improving the fuel rate and greater overall economy. Manufacturers of marine steam turbines will be seeking a market among the remaining types of vessels such as OBO's, LNGC's, and container ships, and other vessels which up to the present have been predominantly diesel engine powered. This will be a difficult task however because for certain types of vessel the flexibility of operation and the better off-design fuel rate of diesel installations is more appropriate to their service requirements.

Although such innovations as steam generation by "fluid bed combustion" and "combined steam and gas cycle" are being re-appraised, and the concept of "reheat" and "complex feed heating cycles" etc are being reconsidered, the chief advantages of the steam plant will still be the low grade of fuel which can be burnt, the inherent reliability, and the freedom from noise and vibration.

It seems inevitable that there will be a reduction in the total number of steam turbine propulsion units required in the immediate future, and with the laying-up of a large part of the world tanker fleet, there will be fewer steam turbine units in service, but it is unlikely that there will be no future for the steam turbine propulsion unit if manufacturers are able to meet the challenge of changing requirements in the marine industry.

Part II—Inspection, Trouble-shooting and Case Histories

There are a number of different designs of early turbines still in use, but modern turbines are not different basically from the earlier ones, and a number of problems are common to all turbines.

8. AN EXTERNAL EXAMINATION OF THE TURBINE WHEN RUNNING

8.1. STEAM OR LUBRICATING OIL LEAKS
Apart from being wasteful, both are potential hazards in an engine room space.

8.2. LAGGING
Reduction of heat losses with properly lagged casings, particularly the HP turbine is important to reduce the possibility of casing distortion, and to maintain a cooler engine space. This also applies to steam pipes.

8.3. STEAM PIPE FORCES AND RESTRAINTS
To keep pipe forces on the turbine down to a minimum piping such as main steam pipes should not be fixed rigidly, or restrained rigidly at positions near the turbine flanges.

Bled steam pipes, and lubricating oil pipes should not be run so as to restrain the natural thermal expansion of a turbine casing in the axial direction.

9. AN INTERNAL EXAMINATION OF THE TURBINE

9.1. EROSION OF BLADING

9.1.1. Ahead Blading

The last two or three stages in a condensing turbine could be subject to erosion damage, because to achieve the best possible thermal efficiency, expansion of the steam into the saturated region is necessary.

It is not the "fog" of water particles in this region which causes the damage, but the larger droplets formed when the particles (less than $0 \cdot 2 \ \mu$ in diameter) coalesce on the fixed blades forming rivulets which flow over the surface and break away at the trailing edges. By this time the droplets are $100 \ \mu$ to $500 \ \mu$ in diameter, and are too large to accelerate with the steam. Consequently they strike the moving blade on the back of the leading edge and remove metal at a rate which is proportional to the near cube of the impact velocity.

It is usual in present-day designs to provide water extraction channels in the annular space between fixed blades in the final stages so that water centrifuged off the moving blades can be collected and drained away. Some manufacturers also fit stellite shields on the leading edges of the last two or three moving blades in the LP turbine to reduce the rate of erosion to the minimum.

Turbine designers are well aware of the dangers of erosion, and one of the main design parameters of the LP turbine is the limitation of the last stage tip speed to avoid erosion damage. The cost of machining blades from special steels or of providing stellite shields has to be carefully balanced against other limitations for a given power output.

One manufacturer has reported that the weight loss with time dw/dt is equal to $K(V - V_t)^h$ where K is a constant, V is the impact velocity, V_t the threshold velocity, and "h" is an exponent of the order $2 \cdot 5$ to $3 \cdot 0$. The threshold velocity is that below which significant erosion does not occur. It varies from 300 ft per second for mild steel to 1000 ft per second for certain special steels and stellite. The manufacturer's turbines were reported as limited to a last stage blade tip speed of 1325 ft per second.

More recently it has been suggested* that erosion can be almost eliminated by correct choice of nozzle and blade flow path and increased axial gap between them, the hypothesis being that the further away the moving blades are from the fixed blades (or

---

* A means of estimating the erosion hazard in low-pressure steam turbines Brown–Boveri Review 58, 1971, (10) 458–472.

nozzles) the more time the water droplets have to accelerate to achieve the same velocity as the steam. The long-established criterion of blade peripheral velocity is no longer important according to this analysis.

The incidence of erosion in modern marine turbines has been very small, and cases where it became significant were usually due to operation at low superheat temperatures, high vacuum, lack of or inadequate water extraction channels, blocked draining orifices, or combinations of all these factors over a period of time.

If lacing wires are located near to the eroded leading edges of reaction blades there is a danger of blade or lacing wire failure. Any cases of serious blade erosion should be further investigated in the light of the above remarks regarding faulty operation or control.

9.1.2. Astern Blading

If there has been extensive erosion of ahead blading resulting from high moisture content, it may be found that astern blading is also eroded due to water droplets forming on the outer casing and dripping into the exhaust end of the astern casing.

It will be appreciated that when the astern turbine is turning ahead, it tends to act like a compressor, drawing in the drips of water falling past the exhaust, which erode the astern wheel blades in much the same manner as in the ahead stages, except that the water drops strike the trailing edges of the astern blades. There may be more incidence of this effect when both ahead and astern exhausts are adjacent and the flow is downward into the condenser than in the case of the axial exhaust LP turbine where both ahead and astern casings exhaust in one direction downstream.

9.2. FOULING OF BLADES WITH DEPOSITS

Boiler salts can enter the turbine in three ways:

a) By priming. When the concentration of boiler solids is high there is a tendency of the water to foam. Bubbles explode on the surface carrying over tiny drops of water into the superheater and on into the turbine.

b) By taking over a quantity of water as a result of heavy rolling also by allowing the water level to drop to a low level, resulting in an increase in the pressure in the drum. Make-up water pumped in rapidly cools the water in the drum and the resulting drop in pressure may cause the drum to fill rapidly with water and overflow in large quantities.

c) In a closed system consisting of water containing dissolved matter, in equilibrium with the vapour, the dissolved matter distributes itself quantitatively between the vapour and the water, in a ratio which depends on the nature of the dissolved matter and the temperature and pressure of the system. (This ratio is called the distribution ratio, and it increases as the temperature is raised.)

At boiler pressures of $850 \, \text{lbs/in}^2$ or above the effect becomes significant with regard to silica. In effect the silica becomes volatile in steam. The presence of caustic soda reduces the ratio for silica, but if the silica content is not kept at low levels, it will be carried over in quantity and precipitated out at some stage in the turbine and be deposited on the blades.

The incidence of b) is probably small these days when drums are arranged fore and aft, but the thermal shock stresses attendant on "slugs" of water quenching nozzles, blading and rotor is much more serious than any deposition of salts and there is also a likelihood of thrust bearing failures, due to the sudden axial force exerted on the rotor.

9.2.1. Deposits

During some experiments on land sets it was found that salts had precipitated in areas of the turbine roughly as follows

Sulphate	In early HP turbine zone
Sodium	Around the 316°C are a (melting point 318°C).
Chloride	A little lower down the turbine.
Iron	All through the machine.
Silica	Lower HP zone and downstream.

The pressure was 1175 lbs/in^{2}g and 516°C at the superheat outlet. On this 60 MW machine a total of 7·7 lb of deposit per annum was estimated, or equivalent to a deposit of 0·0026 lb per 10^6 lb of steam.

Deposits on moving blades reduce the flow passages and increase the pressure difference across the blades. If the deposition is extensive there is a risk of overloading the thrust bearing.

Nozzle steam impulses increase in intensity with fouling and could lead to moving blade failures from metal fatigue where previously the design limits against failure were satisfactory.

Deposits on nozzles also increase the pressure drop across the nozzles and increase the diaphragm deflection, setting up larger stresses which could result in permanent distortion due to creep. There is a general deterioration in performance of the turbine due to reduced efficiency.

Again, experiments on land sets have indicated that by suitably reducing the boiler outlet temperature and pressure over a period of some hours, the state point is moved closer to the saturation line and in this way wet steam washing on load can be carried out. Such a system might be adopted for marine practice. It is reported that 85 per cent of the turbine can be washed in this way with no erosion damage.

9.3. Rubbing of Labyrinth Glands

There are two types of labyrinth glands, the atmospheric gland and the interstage gland. Both types work in the same way by throttling the steam between the shaft and the gland knife-edge, but the atmospheric glands are more numerous because at the inlet end of the HP turbine they usually have to throttle the steam from the first stage nozzle outlet pressure down to atmospheric pressure. There are many designs of shaft glands, but probably the most common type at present is that of the spring back knife-edge segments in the housing which are replaceable.

Up to temperatures of 399°C leaded-nickel-bronze glands are normally used of composition nickel 12–14 per cent, zinc 18–20 per cent, tin 15–25 per cent, lead 4–5 per cent, iron 1–5 per cent (max.), phosphorous 0–2 per cent, manganese 0–5 per cent (max.), the remainder copper.

On occasions this material has been used up to 482°C plus, but at these higher temperatures rapid de-zincification and resulting cracking may occur which could lead to severe shaft damage if rubbing took place. 13 per cent chromium stainless iron gland material is generally used above operating temperatures of 427°C.

Knife edges cut on the shaft will be easily damaged in handling the rotor and can only be re-cut with difficulty and then only to a limited diameter. On the other hand, knife edges on the shaft are said to dissipate the heat generated more rapidly when the glands rub.

Gland rubbing can occur as a result of (a) casing thermal distortion, (b) a thermal bend in the rotor, (c) displacement of the casing relative to the bearings due to pipe thrusts or moments.

Theoretically a bent shaft should be the only circumstance under which rubbing aggravates the bend by heating the outward bowed perimeter of the shaft and increasing the bend in that direction, but rubbing of a straight shaft can induce a thermal bend under certain circumstances, particularly if the running speed corresponds with a shaft critical whirling speed, when the slightest temperature differential across a diameter could cause instability of the shaft. If a rub has continued long enough on a straight shaft the temperature distribution along the shaft will eventually become unequal and again a thermal bend will result.

If a permanent bend results it is interesting to note that when cool the shaft will be bowed in the opposite direction to the sector of the rotor which has rubbed. This is because the outer skin of the rotor has yielded in compression when heated locally by the rub and pulls the rotor into a bent condition with the rub on the concave side when cool.

9.4. RUBBING OF MOVING BLADE TIP SEALS

9.4.1. Axial Rubbing

Because impulse-type stages are usually designed for some percentage of reaction, axial tip sealing and shrouding of the moving blades is necessary to reduce flow losses over the tip. The tip seals are either part of the shrouding, or projections from the diaphragms onto the shrouding with small clearances at the inlet stages gradually increasing downstream. Some designs also have radial sealing which acts in the same manner.

The thrust bearing is usually located at the steam inlet end of a turbine, so that when steam is admitted working up to service power the rotor which is heated more rapidly than the larger mass of the casing expands at a faster rate than the casing, and the rotor discs and blades move away from the diaphragms increasing the axial clearance. Since the casing expands less rapidly it will be some time before conditions are stable and clearances are once more restored to near the original value.

When power is being reduced the opposite effect takes place. Closing in the manoeuvring valve or throttle valves, the steam is throttled to a lower temperature and pressure and the rotor is cooled more rapidly than the casing, and axial clearances are reduced. It is important to realise therefore that particularly in the case of the HP turbine where rotors are a relatively small mass compared with the casing and its insulation, the differential expansion is the important parameter (i.e. the expansion or contraction of the rotor relative to the casing). (LP turbines may well have a reverse relationship of masses.) Thus an indicator which shows only casing expansion is of only limited value. Differential expansion should be indicated at the end furthest from the thrust bearing, and set at zero when casing and rotor are at the same temperature cold, indicating a positive or negative differential. A negative differential expansion will reduce rotor/diaphragm clearances when the thrust bearing is at the steam inlet end.

In general, therefore, if an axial rub has occurred the cause will be reduced clearance from a rapid drop in the steam temperature which is also related to the different rates of temperature change of casing and rotor, or it could be due to incorrect adjustment of clearances when first installed, or at a later time after maintenance.

The checking of clearances will only be correct when both rotor and casing are at the same temperature, and various angular positions of the rotor should be tried to see if clearances are the same all round.

Axial rubbing could overheat shrouding, diaphragms, or blade roots if there is a blade root seal as well as a tip seal, possibly causing local yield and distortion.

9.4.2. Blade Tip Rubbing

The last few stages of an LP turbine embody stages with a high percentage of reaction and although shrouding would also be an advantage to prevent tip leakage the length of the blades employed and their shape do not always enable shrouding to be fitted.

In such cases tip leakage is prevented by designing for clearances possibly as small as 0·6 mm between casing (or diaphragm rim extension) and moving blade tips.

The tips of the moving blades are machined to provide fine edges so that if radial tip rubbing should occur the blade tip will be worn away without damage to the blade.

Some designs of LP casing are integral with an underslung downward flow single or dual condenser and the rotor incorporates the astern turbine. During manoeuvring operations going ahead and astern, the LP casing is often subject to thermal distortion and the blade tips may touch the casing. If lacing wires are incorporated, the rubbing could put a strain on the brazing between wire and blade, and cause failure of the brazing. [Some land sets incorporate what is termed catenary shrouding on the last stage long tapered and twisted blades. Lengths of shrouding riveted between the tips are curved radially inward in the form of a catenary, so that the centrifugal force of rotation sets up a purely compressive stress along the length of each shroud piece.]

9.5. BLOCKAGE OF BLED STEAM OR WATER EXTRACTION DRAINS

It is important that bleed belt drains, and water extraction belt drains are kept open and free of scale and other debris. They are usually orifices led by a pipe to an atmospheric drain tank, or directly through the bottom of the inner casing into the condenser. LP casings almost always have water collector channels between the last few stages. The wet steam droplets centrifuged to these channels coalesce and flow down to the bottom where they pass through a drain orifice. If these holes are blocked, the channels fill with water until they spill over into the next stage, causing erosion damage to the moving blades, particularly at the tips.

Bleed belts can, under certain circumstances, fill with water, and unless drains are clear this can cause not only a local thermal shock on the casing and blades but could also distort the turbine cylinder sufficiently to case interstage gland rubbing.

Drains led to a drain tank can be easily tested for blockage, but the type which drains directly into the condenser is difficult to test for blockage without lifting out the rotor. The only test in these conditions is to pour water into the drain channels and look to see if the water drains out into the condenser.

9.6. LACING WIRE BRAZING FAILURE, DAMPING WIRE WEAR

Lacing wires are used primarily to prevent certain modes of moving blade vibration which may otherwise cause fatigue failures. A number of blades are secured to one another by brazing the wire to each blade, a process which should be closely controlled in the building stage to ensure that the braze material runs well into the hole and fills the spaces between the wire and the hole by capillary action, leaving neat fillets on both sides of the blade. If, for any reason, the holes are not adequately filled, the brazing may fail after a period of running and one or more blades is then no longer inhibited and may be able to vibrate on its own.

Damping wires do not prevent blade vibration but merely limit the amplitude at resonance by providing dry friction damping. These wires are not brazed to the blades and may be single-pitch lengths, or cover a number of blades depending upon the manufacturer's design.

One manufacturer has used crimped metal tubing instead of wires brazed to the blades, to avoid the problems which are often associated with brazing, as already mentioned.

9.7. Failure of Fixed Blading or Nozzles

If fixed blades, such as are found in 50 per cent reaction turbines, break off they will cause damage to moving and fixed blades downstream.

There is unlikely to be failure of the identical fixed blades due to vibration because steam bending stresses are usually low and there is no centrifugal force on the blades.

Diaphragm nozzles sometimes break away at the trailing edges. If the trailing edges are sharp-edged, large stress concentrations could cause cracks to run into the fixed blades as a result of thermal stresses from carry-over or water thrown up from an undrained bled steam belt. The pressure difference across a diaphragm causes it to deflect like a uniformly loaded semi-circular disc simply supported at the rim. The nozzles are usually the weakest section of the diaphragm and the maximum deflection is always at the corners of the bore supporting the sealing glands. The highest stresses are usually in the nozzles at an angle somewhere between the vertical and horizontal axes symmetrical about the vertical axis. If a row of moving blades with axial seals rubs hard on the downstream side of the diaphragm it is possible that plastic yield of the diaphragm due to the localized heating could result in a permanent deformation of the diaphragm, causing the centre to deflect downstream. In addition there are the steady-state and transient thermal stresses to be considered.

On occasions it may be necessary to machine out a row of moving blades as a temporary measure leaving the roots in place. In these circumstances, if the corresponding fixed row of blades or nozzles is not damaged, they should be left in place to drop the pressure before the next set of fixed blades, otherwise excessive pressures may be set up which could cause damage to diaphragms downstream.

9.8. Warp of Horizontal Joints

It is sometimes found that when the top and bottom half HP casings are parted the horizontal joint is no longer flat. A straight edge placed diametrically across the flanges may show the outer edge of the flange to be higher than the inner, and in some instances the joint has been made good again by filing and scraping the flange faces to meet flat.

In fact, this is not necessary because the cause of the warp is high temperature creep of the inner fibres of the casing in compression and making good the joints will allow further creep to take place later. The joints should be left alone and the horizontal joint bolts pulled up hard to close the gap on the inside. Remaking of the flanges will only be necessary where it is found that there has been leakage which has wire-drawn the flange face, and under those circumstances the manufacturer should be consulted. The leakage may have been caused by creep in the joint bolts, relieving the stress on the inside edge of the flange, and allowing a gap to appear when reducing steam flow and temperature.

10. AN INTRODUCTION TO BLADE AND WHEEL VIBRATION

10.1. BLADE VIBRATION

Blade vibration is an important feature of turbines, for if one considers that there may be upwards of 3000 blades in a compound turbine, and the failure of a single blade could put half the unit out of action, it is perhaps not surprising that most manufacturers devote special attention to this subject. Regrettably, however, blade failures do still occur.

10.1.1. Blades

Most modern turbines have impulse, or impulse-reaction blading with an increasing percentage of reaction through the HP turbine and also the LP turbine. The last three to four stages in LP turbines are usually twisted and tapered along their length. Each stage of blading is preceded by a group of nozzles, a full circle, except for the first stage which is usually a Curtis wheel, the inlet nozzles being of the partial admission type. Not many first stage blading failures occur, the blades being very short. Fundamental frequencies are usually far in excess of any excitation which may be present.

10.1.2. Disks

The wheels on to which the moving blades are fixed vibrate like a disk in the plane of the wheel, the blading and shrouding acting like an extension of the wheel.

10.1.3. Blade Shrouding, Lacing Wires, Damping Wires

Impulse-reaction blading is usually shrouded with a cover band fixed to the blade tips. Although the function of the shrouding is to prevent steam losses over the blade tips, it also serves to inhibit vibration if properly designed. Lacing wires on the other hand are fitted and fastened to each blade specifically to inhibit certain modes of vibration. Damping wires are not fastened to blades, but limit the amplitude of vibration.

10.1.4. Blade Roots

There are many methods by which blades are fixed to the wheel. Figure 49 illustrates some of the more common forms of root fixing in use today. Blade vibration characteristics depend upon the type of root employed so far as frequencies, damping and vibration stresses are concerned. At the same time since blades are subjected to high centrifugal force when the wheels rotate, the roots and wheel rims must be capable of

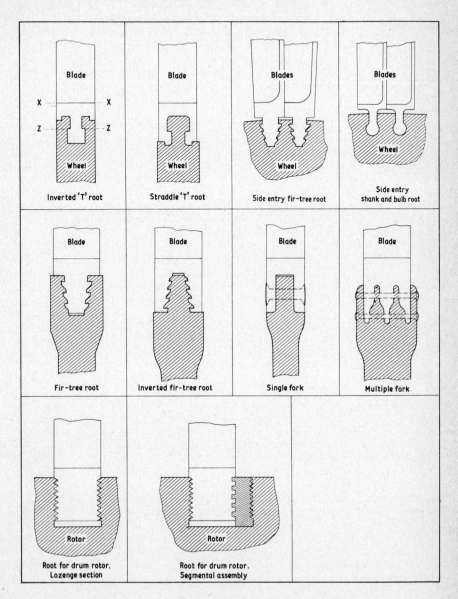

FIG. 49.—*Various types of root fixing for turbine blades.*

withstanding high centrifugal (steady) stresses. Some manufacturers have a standard size root for various blade lengths of the same profile. In this way a rotor can be fitted with blade lengths appropriate to each stage depending on the steam cycle requirements of individual owners. One manufacturer, for example, uses 24 different blade lengths from 12·6 mm to 67 mm employing an identical root size and blade profile for each. From the tooling and quantity production aspect cost will be reduced, but other problems are introduced as will be described elsewhere in the paper. The design of the root fixing is a most important feature.

10.1.5 Modes of Blade Vibration

Strictly, blade vibration should always be considered in terms of the total dynamic system of wheels and rotor since resonant frequencies, damping, and energy distribution are all affected by the system. For convenience, however, it is acceptable to think of a single blade, or "packets" of blades when referring to the various modes of vibration.

10.1.6. Single Blades

When a single blade is clamped at the root and vibrated at its lowest natural frequency, the mode of vibration will be similar to a prismatic bar (Fig. 50(a)), the maximum amplitude being at the tip, the maximum stress being at the root. The direction of vibration will be perpendicular to the axis corresponding to the minimum moment of inertia. The chord of a turbine blade is usually at an angle to the plane of the turbine wheel, hence the axis of the minimum moment of inertia will also be angularly displaced (Fig. 50(b)). This is known as the "flapwise" fundamental mode of vibration (or fundamental tangential mode when referred to the rim of the wheel).

Modes of vibration in the flapwise direction continue from the fundamental to the first, second, third, etc., harmonics (Fig. 50(c)) with one, two, three, etc., nodes, each at correspondingly higher frequencies. For prismatic bars, if the fundamental frequency is n cycles/sec., the first harmonic will be $n \times 6·39$ c/s, the second harmonic $n \times 17·5$ c/s, the third harmonic $n \times 34·3$ c/s and so on.

In a similar manner (Fig. 50(d)) the single blade can vibrate at its lowest natural frequency in an "edgewise" direction in a plane perpendicular to the axis of minimum moment of inertia (axial fundamental mode when referred to the rotor wheel). The edgewise fundamental frequency is usually higher than the flapwise fundamental. The ratio of the flapwise frequency to the edgewise frequency is approximately equal to the square root of the ratio of minimum to maximum moment of inertia of the blade section. Again the other modes of vibration are the first, second, third, etc., harmonics.

The third form of vibration of a single blade is the torsional fundamental mode in which the tip swings torsionally about a radial axis termed the centre of twist. The frequency of the fundamental mode is usually higher than either of the other two, and again there are higher harmonics with nodes at positions up the blade, sections of the blade either side of a node swinging in anti-phase.

Each of the modes mentioned has a discrete frequency. At high frequencies, it may be, for example, that one of the harmonics is very close to another harmonic of a different mode. In that case the blade will vibrate in some mixed mode condition, at the common frequency.

10.1.7. Packets of Shrouded Blades

Blades linked together with a shrouding strip (or shroud band, or cover-band) are termed a "batch" of "packet" and behave in much the same way as single blades except

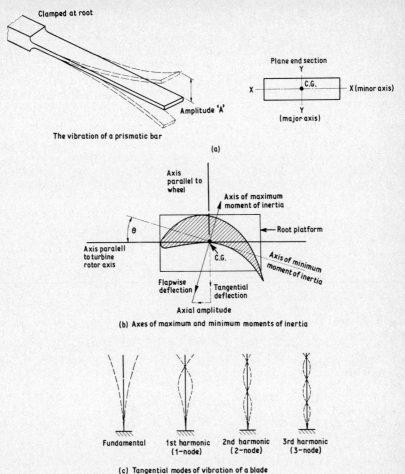

Clamped at root

Amplitude 'A'

The vibration of a prismatic bar

Plane end section
Y
X —— • C.G. —— X (minor axis)
Y
(major axis)

(a)

Axis parallel to wheel

Axis of maximum moment of inertia

θ

Axis paralell to turbine rotor axis

Root platform

C.G.

Axis of minimum moment of inertia

Flapwise deflection

Tangential deflection

Axial amplitude

(b) Axes of maximum and minimum moments of inertia

Fundamental   1st harmonic   2nd harmonic   3rd harmonic
                (1-node)   (2-node)   (3-node)

(c) Tangential modes of vibration of a blade

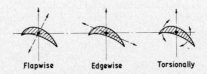

Flapwise   Edgewise   Torsionally

(d) Three modes of vibration of a blade

FIG. 50.—*Blade vibration. (a) Vibration of a prismatic bar. (b) Axes of maximum and minimum moments of inertia. (c) Tangential modes of vibration of a blade. (d) Three modes of vibration of a blade.*

that in addition to the three fundamental types of vibration in which all blades in the batch vibrate in-phase with each other in the flapwise, edgewise, and torsional directions, a further three types are introduced. These are the clamped-pinned modes of flapwise, edgewise and torsional vibration. The edgewise and torsional modes of vibration are rather more complex, however, since the two are often coupled. They do not behave exactly like the flapwise modes.

The name clamped-pinned is something of a misnomer too because the tips are not truly pinned nor the roots truly clamped. The shrouding introduces a small restoring couple on the tips, dependent upon the shroud to tenon fixing stiffness.

The feature of the clamped-pinned mode is that there are a number of ways in which the individual blades in a packet can vibrate relative to one another, i.e. in different phase relationships. Each phase relationship exists at a discrete frequency within a frequency band. They are called collectively the clamp-pinned modes.

Figure 51 shows curves of frequency ratio of the packet fundamental tangential frequency, the packet clamped-pinned frequency and the first harmonic packet frequency, in terms of the dimensionless rigidity ratio:—

$$\frac{\text{(rigidity of 1 pitch of shrouding)}}{\text{(rigidity of 1 blade)}} = \left(\frac{pI_B E_B}{L I_S E_S} \right)$$

where

p = shroud pitch (mm)
L = blade length (mm)
I_B = blade minimum moment of inertia (mm^4)
I_S = shroud minimum moment of inertia (mm^4)
$E_B = E_S$ (usually) = modulus of elasticity of blade
 and shroud material (kg/mm^2)

and the dimensionless mass ratio:

$$\frac{\text{(Mass of 1 pitch of shrouding)}}{\text{(Mass of 1 blade)}}$$

where frequency ratio is the frequency of the packet divided by the frequency of a single blade.

Looking at Fig. 51 it can be seen that in a packet of six blades there are six fundamental tangential modes of vibration. If, for example, the rigidity ratio were 0·2, and the mass ratio were 0·2, then the first mode would be the fundamental tangential in-phase mode, at a frequency ratio of 1·0, all blades swinging together. The other five modes would occur in a band of closely-grouped frequencies between a frequency ratio of 4·5 and 4·9, and their swinging form would be of the clamped-pinned type. Similarly there are six first harmonic tangential modes of vibration. The first, where all blades are swinging in-phase, with a node about two-thirds up each blade, occurs at a frequency ratio of about 5·8, while the other five (not shown) will be similar to the fundamental clamped-pinned modes, but each blade will have a node about half-way up its effective length. Similar relationships exist for packets containing more than six blades of the same dimensions, but it is of interest to note that although there will be $(m-1)$ clamped-pinned modes (where m is the number of blades in a packet) the frequency ratio upper and lower limits (4·5 to 4·9 in the example given above) will be virtually unchanged, so there will be $(m-1)$ discrete frequencies more closely bunched together.

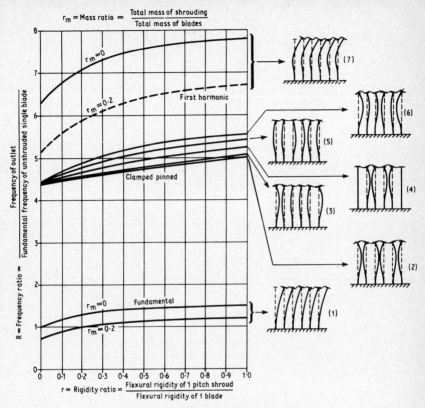

FIG. 51.—*The tangential vibrations of a packet of six blades.*

Thus, if the single blade frequency is known together with the mass and rigidity ratios, it is possible to predict the packet fundamental clamped-pinned, and first harmonic frequencies with reasonable accuracy, as a first approximation.

Similar relationships apply to packets of blades in which the predominant swinging form is of the axial or torsional type, so a suitable method of labelling each mode is clearly necessary.

One system in use today refers to the clamped-pinned modes as the out-of-phase modes, and thus, for a packet of six blades the fundamental tangential in-phase mode is labelled 1 T.I.P., and the five clamped-pinned modes the 1 T.O.P. modes, standing for "fundamental tangential out-of-phase modes". The first harmonic tangential in-phase becomes 2 T.I.P., and the first harmonic tangential clamped-pinned type modes become the 2 T.O.P. modes, etc. Similarly the fundamental axial in-phase mode becomes 1 A.I.P., and the axial clamped-pinned type modes become 1 A.O.P. Finally there are the 1 Tor.I.P. and 1 Tor.O.P. modes representing the fundamental torsional modes.

A suitable method, which would be more definitive would include the swinging form type. For example, the fundamental tangential in-phase mode would become

1 T.I.P. (C-F), where (C-F) refers to the clamped-free cantilever fundamental swinging form, and (C-P) would refer to the clamped-pinned cantilever swinging form, so that the above would become 1 T.O.P. (C-P), 2 T.I.P. (C-F), 2 T.O.P. (C-P), 1 A.I.P. (C-F), etc.

10.1.8. Excitation

The most common form of excitation is the steam impulse which a moving blade experiences as it passes the stationary blades, or nozzles. With the exception, perhaps, of the first stage, where groups of nozzles are concentrated over a small arc of the circumference, and therefore exert considerable steam force on the moving blades, this is probably the strongest form of excitation the blade will be subjected to, particularly in the H.P. turbine. Other forms of excitation are those from mechanical sources transmitted through the rotor from claw couplings (not used in modern turbines) and gearing. Not many cases exist, however, with proven mechanical excitation as the exclusive cause of moving blade failure.

Steam excitation can also result from variations in flow, or pressure, or both, around the circumference of a diaphragm, due to obstructions in the flow path, bled-steam extraction holes, or localized eddies in the flow path. If this variation is known, harmonic analysis of the distribution may reveal a component which could excite blades. The longer L.P. turbine blades are more prone to excitation from these sources.

10.1.9. Damping

There are three sources of damping when the blades are working under operating conditions:—

a) Internal damping of the material used in the manufacture of blades.
b) Inherent dry friction damping of the blade assembly at root and tip.
c) Fluid or viscous damping of the steam environment.

It is usual to consider the dynamic magnification factor "Q", however, since this is the quantity which is often measured in vibration testing of blades and refers to the stress magnification at resonance.

Vibration tests to determine damping are not carried out during running conditions so the fluid damping is an unknown component as also is the effect upon root fixing when subjected to centrifugal force. A newly assembled rotor may have higher blade damping properties than one which has been running for a period in service due to the accumulation of oxide and fretting products in way of the structural joins.

Values of "Q" used in calculations vary, but a somewhat empirical value of 100 is sometimes quoted which is intended to include all three sources mentioned above.

One simple method of determining the dynamic magnification factor in a static test when the shape of the resonance curve has been determined from blade vibration tests, is shown in Fig. 52. By this means the author has measured a relative value of $Q_0 = 500$ on a newly bladed rotor.

10.2. WHEEL VIBRATION

If wheels and shrouded blades be thought of as an integral disc, they also have definite modes of vibration.

10.2.1. Nodal Diameters

If a disc is held rigidly at the centre and an impulse is given to some point on the rim, waves will travel round the rim in both clockwise and anti-clockwise directions. Suppose

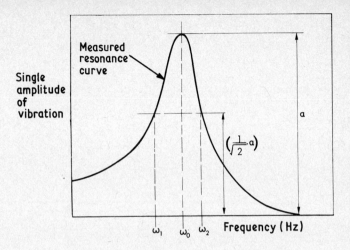

Since Q_0 = dynamic magnification factor at resonance

$$Q_0 = \frac{\omega_0}{\omega_1 - \omega_2} = \frac{f_0}{f_1 - f_2}$$

where f_0 = resonance frequency.

f_1 and f_2 = frequencies on either side of the resonant frequency at which the amplitude is $\dfrac{1}{\sqrt{2}} \times$ amplitude at resonance.

FIG. 52.—*Single amplitude of vibration.*

the wave lengths to be $2\pi r$, there will be two nodes on the rim diametrically opposite each other and at $\pm 90°$ from the source of the impulse.

The movement of a point diametrically opposite the source of the impulse will be 180° out of phase with the direction of movement of the source. If now the two nodes at the rim are joined by a line through the centre, the disc is said to have one nodal diameter.

Similarly, if the source frequency were increased until the travelling ripples had a wave length of πr, they would reinforce each other as they coincided, such that four nodes would occur round the rim. If these nodes were then joined diametrically, the disc would have two nodal diameters, and so on, each section between the nodal diameters moving in anti-phase with its neighbour (Fig. 53(a)). It is usual in design of the wheel to ensure that wheel modes up to 4 nodal diameters cannot be steam-excited to vibrate within the running speed range, to avoid wheel fatigue failure. Higher modes require a larger energy input to excite them.

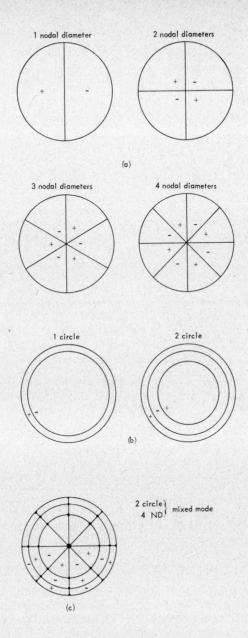

FIG. 53.—*Nodal diameters.*

10.2.2. Nodal Circles

If the disc is held at the centre and vibrated at that position the rim will vibrate in anti-phase in much the same manner as a cantilever when vibrated at its base. The fundamental mode, called the umbrella mode, occurs at low frequency. As the frequency is increased to the equivalent of the first harmonic frequency of a cantilever, a circular node appears on the disk. This is the one-nodal circle.

Increase the frequency still further and at a discrete resonant frequency two circular nodes appear, and so on. Areas between the nodal circles move in anti-phase with each other (Fig. 53(b)).

10.2.3. Mixed Nodes

It often happens that nodal diameter frequencies and nodal circle frequencies coincide, and a complex pattern of both circles and diameters occurs (Fig. 53(c)).

10.2.4. Blade and Wheel Vibration

Blades attached to the wheel rim form an extension of the wheel in terms of wheel vibration and must be considered as part of a complete coupled system. If blade and wheel vibrations occur at the same frequency they interact one upon the other modifying each slightly. When a bladed wheel is acted upon by steam excitation to vibrate in the nodal-diameters mode, waves run backwards at the rotational speed round the rim and blades (relative to the casing, the nodal diameters remain fixed).

10.3. BLADE VIBRATION UNDER OPERATING CONDITIONS

Although the primary object of turbine blading is to turn the rotor when steam jets are directed on to them, they must also be strong enough to withstand the various forces acting upon them in the process, in a particular type of environment.

The forces acting upon them are:
a) steam-driving force;
b) centrifugal force;
c) vibratory forces;

At the same time they may be affected by temperature, humidity, and possibly corrosive chemicals.

10.3.1. The Steam Driving Force which actually provides the turning moment on the rotor also causes a bending moment on the blade, and if the blade is free-standing and not connected to other blades the bending stress is usually greatest at the root. If it is connected by shrouding to other blades then the position of maximum stress depends upon the restraining moment at the blade tips, and so on. In general, if the force distribution up the length of the blade is known, and the tip and root restraints are known, then it is possible to construct a bending moment diagram and to find the position of maximum bending stress. This stress is usually referred to as the "steady steam bending stress". It will have its greatest positive value on the concave side facing the incoming steam.

10.3.2. The Centrifugal Force is the force on any section up the blade produced by the rotation of the blade. The largest stress will depend upon the shape, radius of rotation and speed of rotation of the blade.

In addition, the centrifugal force can produce a bending stress in the root of the blade if the centre of gravity of the aerofoil section is offset from the root centre of gravity in either the tangential or axial direction, and this can be additive or subtractive to the steady steam bending stress depending upon which way the moment acts.

10.3.3. The Vibratory Forces are steam impulses which strike the blades as they pass in front of each nozzle jet. The partition or wall between each nozzle reduces the velocity of the steam flowing past it due to friction, whereas in the core of the nozzle jet the velocity is a maximum. Thus, a blade moving past the nozzles alternately experiences changes in steam velocity in addition to the steady steam-driving velocity component mentioned in (i).

A moving blade will *always* be subject to the alternating force in addition to the centrifugal steady steam driving force, but when the frequency of the alternating force is equal to a natural frequency of the moving blades, resonance occurs, and the amplitude of vibration of the blades is then dependent upon the amount of damping due to the three separate sources mentioned previously, the magnitude of the vibratory force component, the nozzle/blade pitch phasing, the mode of vibration, and the number of blades in the packet, etc. The vibratory force is usually expressed as a fraction of the steady force, and called the "stimulus" or "excitation".

The amplitude of vibration is related to the stress in the root (or at any other section) by the mode of vibration and the corresponding swinging form of the blade or blades, and it is the stress which is usually quoted when dealing with blade vibration.

Most manufacturers also give some consideration to the vibration characteristics of the blades when they are in the design stage, and again after manufacture they should be vibration-tested to ensure that calculations are confirmed by measured results. On occasions manufacturers neglect the effect of root-fixing, and merely calculate the vibration frequency of the aerofoil section of the blade alone.

Referring back to Fig. 49 for example, if the blade length of the inverted T-root is considered as the distance from the blade tip to the line x.x., the actual frequency under operating conditions will in fact be lower than that calculated because, under the action of centrifugal force when rotating, the blade root jams hard up on the land of the T-root at z.z.; so in effect the actual length of blade now vibrating is no longer the tip to x.x. but tip to z.z. Thus, if a manufacturer has a number of blade lengths with the same root dimensions, then the shorter the blade the greater the percentage error in calculated frequency if the root length is neglected as being an integral part of the vibrating blade.

Root design and manufacture is most important and, ideally, the design engineer should be consulted when manufacturing and fitting methods are being decided. Neither side can work in isolation.

When blades are vibrating under operating conditions, there are a number of factors to be considered:

a) Steam damping and centrifugal force effect on root fixing.
b) Temperature effects.
c) Rotational effects.
d) Steam bending stress.
e) Vibratory stress.
f) Increase in full load torque.
g) LP turbine humidity and stress corrosion.
h) Fretting corrosion.

10.3.4. Steam Damping, Root Fixity Damping

In addition to friction damping and material internal damping, steam damping due to the density of the working fluid takes place. Very little information is available since no comparative environmental tests of steam density damping have been carried out. Centrifugal force effects on the root fixing can change damping characteristics, though very little is known about this subject either.

10.3.5. Temperature Effects

The most important effect of temperature apart from slightly reducing the vibration natural frequency (due to the reduction of the Modulus of Elasticity with increase in temperature) is to reduce the metal fatigue limits, and this must be taken into account when calculating the safety margins against fatigue failure. Usually metal fatigue tests are carried out on test pieces of the blade material early on in the design stage at elevated temperatures. If resonance in blades or wheels occurs at reduced engine speed, then the appropriate fatigue limit at the reduced operating temperature must be used.

10.3.6. Rotational Effects

Rotation increases the natural frequency of blades due to the centrifugal force stiffening effect. This can be reasonably calculated accurately when the blade frequency measured on a static test rig has been determined,[*] though it is usual in computer-aided calculations to incorporate this effect when obtaining each natural frequency for the blade or blade packet.

Since,

$$F_R = \sqrt{F_S^2 + BN^2}$$

where,

$$B = \left(1 \cdot 56 \times \frac{R}{L} + 1 \cdot 17\right)$$

and,

F_R = The frequency at a given rotational speed, (Hz)
F_S = The static blade frequency, (Hz)
N = rotational speed (cycles per second)
R = Radius from shaft centre to blade root fixity position (mm)
L = Blade length from tip to root fixity position (mm)

10.3.7. Steam Bending Stress

The steam bending moment is calculated by considering the tangential steam velocity and the mass flow per blade at small sections up the blade length and obtaining the bending moments at each section. The resultant is found by vector addition, then knowing the root area, the steam bending stress can be calculated. The steam bending stress is roughly proportional to the rotational speed ratio squared. The steam bending stress is referred to as the steady steam bending stress to distinguish it from the vibratory component.

[*] "Vibration of marine turbine blading". R. W. Nolan. SNAME, Feb. 1949.

10.3.8. Vibratory Stress

The vibratory stress is a function of the steady steam bending stress at the resonant speed and is often expressed as

$$\sigma_v = \pm D\sigma_{sb}$$

where

$$D = V_z S_z \alpha_z H_n \left\{ \frac{\nu \text{ (dynamic)}}{\nu \text{ (static)}} \right\}^2$$

$$V_z = \left(\frac{\pi}{\delta}\right) \text{ and } \delta = \text{logarithmic decrement,}$$

$H_n = $ deflection factor ($\leqslant 0\cdot 2$)

$\alpha_z = $ packet factor ($0 \leqslant \alpha_z \leqslant 1\cdot 0$)
(this depends on pitch ratio and phase angle distribution).

$S_z = $ Stimulus, which is dependent upon
     1) Nozzle profile and trailing edge thickness.
     2) Surface finish.
     3) Axial clearance.
     4) Parsons number ratio.
     5) Mach number.
     6) Reynolds number.

A simpler form of relationship assumes that:

$$D = e \times Q$$

where $e = $ steam excitation factor taken as $0\cdot 10$

$$Q = \text{dynamic magnifier (taken as 100)}$$

whereupon

$$D = 10$$

This is a crude expression, however, since it is intended to cover a variety of different blade and nozzle types, and excludes phase relationships, number of blades in a packet, etc. A refinement of this expression includes a "resonant response factor", K, such that,

$$D = K\frac{\pi}{\delta}S$$

where $\delta = $ log decrement, and $S = $ steam excitation, or stimulus fraction.

In effect K is a vibratory stress multiplier which compares the resonant stress of, say, a single clamped-free blade with that of a "packet" of the same blades. Thus the resonant response factor "K" is also a function of the ratio of the number of nozzles (or fixed blades) to the number of moving blades (n/m) the number of blades per packet and the mode of vibration for each order of excitation.

The difficulty in all calculations is not only to obtain the correct calculated steady steam bending stress, but to be able to estimate the exciting force and damping as well. Ideally, manufacturers should have completed tests on their own nozzles and blades under running conditions, and be able to predict the value of "D", applying a factor of safety which is sufficient to cover inaccuracies in calculation and in blade manufacture.

The safety factor is sometimes referred to as "a factor of ignorance", which is possibly an apt interpretation, for it allows some margin for error of assumptions made in the calculations, discrepancies in material properties, manufacturing tolerances, fitting faults, etc. The real criteria of whether a manufacturer has made all the right choices will be his record of success or otherwise over a period of time. In a highly competitive field such as the marine steam turbine industry it is a knife-edge existence between allowing too large a margin for error (and being priced out of the business) and too small a margin leading to a series of costly failures and lost orders.

10.3.9. Increase in Full Load Torque

An aspect of blade vibration (and gearing) not generally appreciated is the effect of hull fouling and roughening, and heavy weather conditions on the shaft torque developed. As the hull resistance increases the engine revolutions at full power tends to decrease, by 3 per cent to 5 per cent in some cases, whereas the shaft torque developed increases. This increase in torque is achieved by an increased steady steam bending force on the blades (leading to increased gear tooth loads also.)

If there is any doubt about the safety of blades against failure, either this factor should be written into the calculations, or, where a torque meter is fitted a maximum limiting torque should be the controlling factor during operation.

10.3.10. LP Turbine Humidity and Stress Corrosion

In the last few stages of an LP turbine the effect of humidity is not known to the author with regard to forces acting on the blades, or damping effects, but it is becoming more apparent that some manufacturers consider the effect of humidity in activating certain corrosive chemicals deposited on the blades as one of the most significant factors in the failure of LP turbine blades in recent years by corrosion fatigue. These blades were calculated to have high factors of safety against failure by conventional standards (F.S. 10).

In the "Wilson line" area of the condition curve where the concentration of boiler salts to water is highest the combination could initiate corrosion leading possibly to corrosion failure. Blades downstream generally operate at higher wetness percentages and it is possible that salts are either not precipitated, or are washed off by the water droplets.

10.3.11. Fretting Corrosion

Fretting fatigue failure has been suggested as a possible cause of failure of some machinery parts, and of blade root failures also. As a general rule the conditions for fatigue failure in a blade root may be satisfied if the fretting occurs at an area of high stress concentration, such as in the radius at a change of section. If there is inadequate clearance in the radius between the male and female sections, fretting could occur. Like corrosion fatigue the normal standards of factors of safety against fatigue failure no longer apply.

10.4. MANUFACTURE AND FITTING

Blades which are fitted to the wheel rim by means of circumferential slots may need some hand-dressing to ensure good butting of adjacent blade roots. Fir-tree roots and variants of the fir-tree type, where a number of "lands" share the centrifugal load must be carefully machined to ensure equal distribution of the load over each land to avoid high crushing stresses.

Whenever hand-dressing is necessary a careful inspection should be made to ensure that no file marks or scratches are made in way of the highly stressed areas near the root. Leading and trailing edges should not be sharp-edged to avoid the effect of notching.

Shrouding should be fitted to suit any inequalities in the pitch of the tenons when the blades are in place, bending or twisting the blades to fit the tenons in the shroud-holes should be avoided. Under no circumstances should tenons be filed down to fit the shroud holes. A strict control of quality of bar stock for manufacture of blades should be maintained at all times.

10.5. BLADE FREQUENCIES AND STRESSES IN OPERATION

When blades have been designed and manufactured, it is usual to carry out blade vibration tests on a packet of blades, and in some cases a fully bladed rotor is vibration-tested both statically and dynamically, but not very often are bladed rotors tested under actual operating conditions.

a) Assume that a packet of blades has been vibration-tested, and resonant frequencies in the static condition are known, together with the calculated static steam bending stresses and centrifugal stresses at full power.

A Campbell diagram (Fig. 54) is plotted which sets down all the vibration frequencies measured during static tests, and the effects of centrifugal stiffening are included.

All known excitation frequencies are then plotted as orders of the rotational speed. If, for example, there are 50 nozzles in a complete ring, a moving blade will experience 50 impulses per revolution, hence the excitation frequency is fiftieth order. Unequal pitch of nozzles at the horizontal joint would be $2 \times$ rotational speed or second order, etc.

Where the order-lines cross the frequency lines, excitation frequency is equal to the blade packet natural frequency, and resonance occurs. There will be many such points and a decision has to be made of the relative importance of each point in terms of blade stresses. To begin with, all points near the service speed will be checked.

Then if

R = speed ratio ($=1\cdot0$ at service speed)
σ_c = root centrifugal stress at service speed (calculated)
σ_{sb} = root steam bending stress at service speed (calculated)
F_c = stress concentration factor in tension at the root
F_b = stress concentration factor in bending at the root.
     (assumed the same value for both steady and vibratory regimes.)

mean stress = $R^2(\sigma_c F_c + \sigma_{sb} F_b)$

vibratory stress $\sigma_v = \pm D\sigma_{sb}F_b$

where

$$D = K\frac{\pi}{\delta}S$$

If the log decrement δ and resonant response factor K for each mode has been measured or calculated for similar blades and shrouding during static vibratory tests, then by taking a value for the steam stimulus fraction of, say, $S = 1/10$ the vibratory stress can be calculated.

The mean and vibratory stresses are then plotted on a metal fatigue limit diagram constructed from values of σ_e and σ_u at the corresponding temperature.

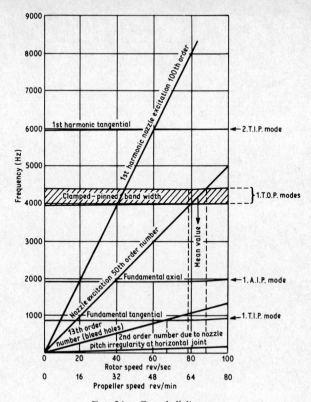

FIG. 54.—*Campbell diagram.*

It is more correct to plot a diagram for each point, the fatigue limit curve being constructed for the operating temperature at resonance (which depends on the speed ratio).

The Goodman and the Gerber limit curves are constructed (Fig. 55) as a function of the vibratory and mean stress components, knowing the vibratory fatigue limit at zero mean stress σ_e and the ultimate stress σ_u at the corresponding temperature. Measured values of fatigue limit usually lie between the Gerber and Goodman lines, therefore the limiting line for failure is taken as the Goodman limit. To allow for manufacturing inequalities and other assumptions, construct a line below the Goodman limit representing a factor of safety of, say, 1·35.

Points which lie below the factor of safety line can be considered as safe under ideal operating conditions, all other factors being equal.

b) Assume that the frequency of the various nodal diameters and circles of the bladed wheels has been measured under rotating conditions, then a wave speed diagram is constructed (Fig. 56) from which the relation between nodal diameters and speed of rotation can be seen and the possible coupling of blade and wheel frequencies. The 4–ND point must be above the running speed.

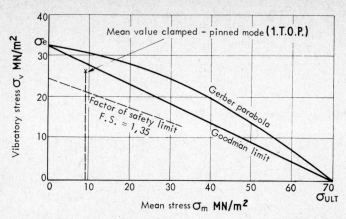

FIG. 55.—*Metal fatigue limit diagram for material at 207°C (fictitious case).*

c) Steps can be taken to limit blade vibration. If the fundamental tangential packet mode is easily excited it may be that there are insufficient blades in a batch.
   If

$$f = \text{frequency of single unshrouded blade (C/S)}.$$
$$m = \text{number of blades in a packet}.$$
$$n = \text{number of revolutions of shaft per second}$$

then since

$$f/mn = \text{wave length} \ (= 1 \cdot 0 \ \text{usually})$$
$$m = f/n$$

10.6. SOME OF THE STEPS WHICH CAN BE TAKEN TO MINIMIZE THE DANGER OF BLADE FATIGUE FAILURES

   a) Change the number of nozzles in the diaphragm.
   b) Skew the nozzle trailing edges to the radial line of the blades.
   c) Eliminate nozzle pitch errors at the horizontal joint or elsewhere round the circumference.
   d) Increase the axial clearance between nozzle trailing edges and moving blade inlet edges.
   e) Avoid the effect of stringers or radial spokes downstream of the last stage blades.*
   f) Increase or decrease the number of bled steam holes downstream or upstream of a row of moving blades, or any such arrangement which causes irregularities in steam flow around the circumference.
   g) Strengthen, and increase the resonant frequencies of the moving blades by reinforcing the blade near the root.

---

* The flow pattern downstream of the last row of moving blades will be affected by the condenser opening and position. If a probe measuring velocity of flow and density were traversed round the circumference it would be possible to carry out a wave analysis and determine the frequencies of the various components together with the relative strength of each harmonic.

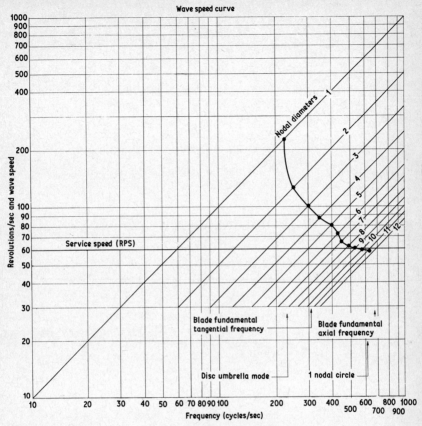

FIG. 56.—*Wave speed diagram.*

h) Thicken the whole profile of the blades and so have fewer and stronger moving blades.

j) Install lacing wires to inhibit clamped-pinned tangential modes.

k) Provide snubbers or damping wires to limit the peak amplitudes at mid-span or at the tips.

Circumstances will dictate which course of action may be necessary, but clearly there may be a number of restrictions to the choice if the turbine has been manufactured and installed before a problem becomes apparent.

11. ROUGH RUNNING OF TURBINE MACHINERY

When a marine steam turbine is first run a number of tests are carried out in the manufacturer's test bay. Generally these spin tests cannot establish much more than that the machine will run satisfactorily up to its maximum speed plus about 10 per cent, coupled to the gearing train. The reason for limited tests is that normally, for large horsepowers, manufacturers have neither the steam capacity nor suitable means to absorb the power in their test bays to run the main propulsion machinery at full load.

The opportunity is taken to set the overspeed trip gear and ensure that this is operational. Checks are made of rotor balance and bearing oil film stability by measuring vibration levels, but short of ensuring that the turbine will turn smoothly when steam is applied, the tests are of little other use. The main sea trials will establish the matching of the propulsion system and propeller and whether full load can be achieved according to the design data. It is only when the full steam flow and inlet steam temperature and pressure are achieved for an adequate period that the turbine machinery can be said to have been properly tested.

11.1. DURING TRIALS

During trials, any rough running which occurs will probably be associated with the high rate of heat flow into the turbine, not apparent during spin testing, such as
a) Casing distortion.
b) Pipe forces.
c) Rotor/gearing misalignment.

11.1.1. Casing Distortion

A turbine casing is far from being a continuous homogenous cylinder. There are horizontal joints requiring thick flanges, a shell of varying diameter, penetrations in the shell for steam inlet and outlet and ends which are re-entrant and penetrated for the rotor. The different masses of metal heat at different rates and distortion becomes extremely complicated to visualize. During transient conditions such as starting up and working up to full power, casing distortion can be quite significant depending upon the rate of increase of power, especially when one considers the fine clearances between fixed and moving parts. If a gland rub occurs, vibration of the rotor may ensue and the turbine should be run at reduced speed until the vibration is within accepted limits and then run up to full power. Persistent vibration from rubbing means that some excessive thermal distortion may be taking place.

100

It may be the presence of water in the bottom half casing, possibly in a bled steam belt which is not properly drained, or it may be that the proper expansion of the casing in an axial or transverse direction is prevented by sticking palm support keys, coming hard up against pipes and other structures, etc., giving rise to displacement of the casing relative to the journal bearings.

11.1.2. Pipe Forces

While HP casings are becoming smaller and more compact, steam pipes are increasing in size and pipe thrusts and moments becoming greater. Torque reaction is also increasing. All these factors make it difficult to prevent the cylinder from lifting off supporting palms, and to provide keying arrangements adequate to allow the casing to expand freely and yet withstand thrusts in various directions. Careful attention should always be paid to the flexibility of the pipework to the turbine, to the position of hangers, clearance of holes through bulkheads for pipes and to pipe expansion movements generally. It may be necessary for powers in excess of, say 29·4 MW (40 000 shp) to copy land practice with separate steam chests and symmetrically arranged inlet steam loop-pipes to the HP casing, for instance. The possible use or pressure-balanced cross-over pipes may also need to be considered in some cases.

Pipe forces which push the turbine casing upwards of sideways may adversely affect the gear shaft/rotor shaft alignment, quite apart from possibly initiating a gland rub.

11.1.3. Rotor/Gearing Misalignment

Gearing pinions and turbine rotors should ideally be in a straight line when running at the maximum design power, yet in most cases the only means to check alignment is when stationary, and cold. If the total relative movement in the vertical and horizontal direction of both the pinion bearings and the turbine bearings can be calculated, then an offset alignment can be made cold. However, the problem is one not only of offset but angle between the axes of the shafts as well, and this is extremely difficult to predict since one needs to know precisely the direction of movement from cold to hot of both pinion bearing centres and both rotor bearing centres.

The side of a gearbox near the turbine will reach temperatures higher than those at the aft side because of the proximity of turbine casing, gland seal pipes, cross-over pipes, etc., and thus displace the pinion bearing centres by different amounts. Similarly, turbine pedestals and engine seatings may not be equally heated. Typical examples of this occur when bleed pipes are placed nearer to one bearing pedestal than another.

Sometimes the bearing pedestals are mounted on box girders which are themselves supported by steel columns. The box girders in way of bled steam pipes are subject to distortion and in turn affect the alignment by tilting the bearing pedestals.

Fine tooth couplings will take up an amount of misalignment, but when transmitting the maximum torque it is possible that the coupling could lock hard, and instead of being truly flexible, becomes a possible source of unbalance at the end of the rotor. Couplings associated with flexible rotors are often a source of rotor vibration, even though each component may be individually properly balanced.

11.2. AFTER A PERIOD OF SATISFACTORY RUNNING

A turbine rotor can develop vibration after a period of satisfactory running and one can state the apparently obvious—something has changed. It may be
  a) Loss of blades, shrouding, lacing wire, closing pieces,
  b) Rubbing,

c) Coupling unbalance,
d) Erosion damage,
e) Deposits of solids on the moving blades.

11.2.1. Loss of Blades, Shrouding Lacing, Closing Pieces

This type of vibration is usually evident by the sudden development of vibration as would be expected. However, the loss of a piece of lacing wire or shrouding may not result in large unbalance. Unless there is a continuous chart recording of vibration level the sudden slight change may go unnoticed.

If vibration monitoring equipment is fitted it may be set to alarm, or to trip beyond predetermined limits depending upon the owner's requirement.

11.2.2. Rubbing

Rubbing, as already mentioned, can be initiated for a number of reasons but after a period of satisfactory running at or near the service speed, when all conditions are stable, gland rubbing is unlikely unless a slug of water passes over from the boiler, and bows the shaft, or water passes over from the boiler, and bows the shaft, or water enters the gland steam and bends the rotor, or water enters the turbine cylinder from a bled steam pipe and distorts the casing or rotor. Very often even during stable conditions such events can occur, but are more likely under transient conditions. Rubbing may go on some time before vibration occurs, unless the speed is near to a rotor critical.

11.2.3. Coupling Unbalance

Coupling unbalance balance over the period of time between inspections can start from an accumulation of sludge in the coupling tube, or wear taking place in the coupling teeth due to inadequate lubrication or both. Whichever the cause, the nature of the build-up of unbalance will be gradual.

11.2.4. Erosion damage

Erosion, as already mentioned, is a gradual process and is generally evenly spread over all blades, so that unbalance due to loss of metal from the moving blades may not be noticeable on the slower running LP rotor in terms of increased vibration.

If, however, blades have been poorly fitted for any reason so that the axial distance from the fixed blades is not the same for all moving blades then those which are nearest the fixed blades will erode more rapidly than the rest and could result in slight unbalance and a gradual build-up of vibration levels.

The most detrimental effect of erosion on balance of a rotor is on the trimming weights placed on the disc of the last stage ahead blades. If water drips from the top half casing into the condenser (at low superheat temperatures) the balance weights will be struck by water droplets and eroded away at the exhaust end. Depending upon the distance of the weights from the axis of rotation, and the magnitude of the weight there will be a slow change in the true balance condition.

11.2.5. Deposits of Solids on the Moving Blades

Deposits of solid matter on the moving blades can upset rotor balance or cause thermal distortion of the rotor due to unequal heat transfer coefficient along blades and at different stages along the rotor.

12. THE BALANCING OF FLEXIBLE ROTORS

12.1. CRITICAL SPEEDS—HISTORICAL INTRODUCTION

Since marine steam turbines are inherently variable-speed machines the question of critical speeds is an important consideration.

It was once common to specify rotor critical speeds as not less than 125 per cent of the design speed. It was thought that in this way rotor criticals could be dismissed as an item of concern in design.

However, it became apparent that the as-built efficiencies were poorer than could be obtained with more moderate shaft sizes and that the internal efficiency of the turbine fell away rapidly because of leakage losses resulting from a high rate of wear of the steam sealing arrangement under abnormal operating conditions. The heavier shafts were more liable to thermal distortion such as bowing, and differential expansion. More important perhaps, there came the realization that the 125 per cent rule did not ensure that the first critical speed was outside the design speed. As better methods of measurement became available it was shown that bearing supports were far from solid as had been assumed in calculations, and that the measured critical speed was always below the calculated value, as seen in Fig. 57, which is a plot of many such measurements. As can be seen, it is impracticable to place an actual critical speed above the running range, unless turbine speeds are greatly reduced from those of long standing practice.

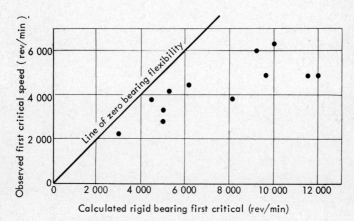

FIG. 57.—*Observed first-critical speeds of turbine rotors.*

103

For example, high pressure turbine rotors are designed to run at about 6500 rev/min at service speed. The 125 per cent rule would call for a calculated rigid bearing critical speed of 8125 rev/min. From Fig. 57 it would actually be between 4000 to 5000 rev/min, or 75 per cent of the service speed. Again, efforts to stiffen the shaft would only result in moving the critical speed nearer to the service speed, but never beyond it.

The reason for the depression of the observed critical speed is the flexibility of the supporting structure of the bearings, and that of the oil film. Contrary to the early methods of calculation, the shaft bearings cannot be considered as nodal points, since they do in fact deflect and the nodes will be outside the bearing span.

Another important characteristic of bearing performance is the strong damping effect of the oil film. It was this damping which permitted trouble-free operation at the critical speed. Thus, the 125 per cent critical speed rule was for may years thought to be achieving its objective since no obvious critical speeds were observed during operation. It was only by deliberately fitting a large unbalance to the stiff rotors of those days that the presence of a critical within the operating range was found.

12.2. BALANCING OF FLEXIBLE ROTORS

Unlike the solid rotors of earlier years, rotors today are more flexiible, with wheels (or discs) integral on small diameter shafts (sometimes called gashed rotors) and are termed over-critical (or super-critical) which means that the operating speed is higher than the first critical speed. (When the operating speed is below the first critical speed it is termed undercritical or sub-critical.)

Some modern high pressure rotors may be over-critical by as much as 50 per cent.

If a flexible rotor is placed in a slow speed balancing machine with "soft" bearing supports, it will behave as though the rotor were a rigid shaft. The shaft will remain straight and vibrate at the resonant frequency of the supports in a mainly transverse plane (Fig. 58(a)) with amplitude $X_A = X_B$.

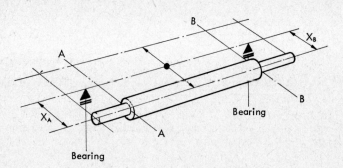

FIG. 58(a).—*Static unbalance.*

This is equivalent to what is known as the static unbalance of the rotor. It will also exhibit the couple or dynamic unbalance, Fig. 58(b) vibrating again in a mainly transverse plane, but with the ends swinging in antiphase with a node at N.

These two rigid modes will occur simultaneously at the resonant frequency of the soft bearing supports. Unbalance can be corrected by placing suitable weights in planes A and B.

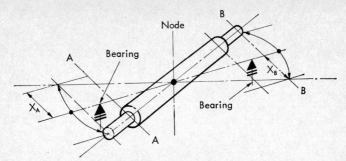

FIG. 58 (b).—*Dynamic unbalance.*

If now the balanced rotor is taken out of the low speed balancing machine and placed in the turbine bearings, the supports will be stiffer, and when the rotor is run up to its first critical speed it will behave as a flexible rotor and take up the deflected shape shown in Fig. 59(a).

If the rotor were run at still higher speeds it would deflect into the second and third modal shapes, Figs. 59(b) and 59(c), with the amplitude of deflection increasing to a maximum at each critical speed.

It is clear that weights placed at planes A and B in Fig. 59(a) will not balance the second flexural mode, and similarly weights placed in planes A and B 180° out of phase in Fig. 59(b) will not balance the third flexural mode, Fig. 59(c). Therefore, careful selection of planes and angles of phase are immediately obvious.

The newly assembled rotor contains a large number of unbalanced masses whose magnitude and position are quite random so the deflection curve of the rotor at a given speed will in general be a three dimensional curve. For convenience the deflection curve and bending moment diagram can be resolved into two planes at right angles fixed relative to the rotor and can be dealt with separately.

The results of passing through critical speeds are
a) The vibration amplitude increases and starts to change in angle relative to some datum point on the rotor.
   As the critical speed is reached the vibration peaks are about 90° out of phase with the force on the bearings. As the critical speed is passed the phase angle increases to 180°.
   In effect, the heavy side of an unbalanced rotor swings inwards towards the axis of rotation as the shaft comes near and passes the first critical speed.
   The light side of the rotor will then be on the outside of the deflection curve until the second critical speed is passed when it will once again turn through 180° so that the heavy side is on the outside.
b) Although theory shows that the vibration amplitudes increase to infinity at the critical speed, bearing oil film damping forces prevent this from happening.
c) Between the first and second critical the rotor tends to rotate about its mass centre, so that vibrations will tend to decrease.
d) Because of the rapid change of vibration phase and amplitude at a critical speed a rotor running at the critical speed is extremely sensitive to small changes in conditions such as speed, and temperature. Consequently it is difficult to balance a rotor at the critical speed and critical speeds should be designed away from manoeuvring speeds.

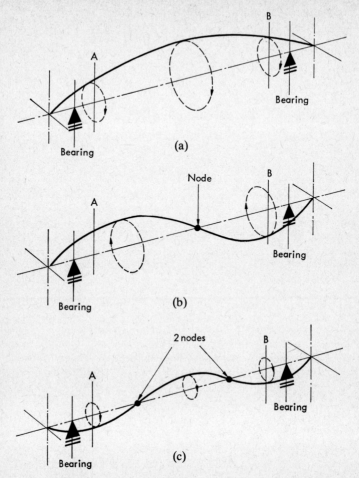

FIG. 59.—(a) First flexural mode. (b) Second flexural mode. (c) Third flexural mode.

12.3. METHODS OF ACHIEVING BALANCE

One method* used for the balancing of flexible rotors which gives satisfactory results briefly as follows:

a) The rotor, Fig. 60(a), is balanced as a rigid rotor in a slow speed balancing machine with force and couple balance weights added, Figs. 60(b) and 60(c).

b) The rotor is run near to its first flexural mode critical speed and weights are added as illustrated in Fig. 55(d). The effect of these weights is to compensate for the modal unbalance, but not to disturb the rigid rotor force balance of Figs. 60(b) and 60(c).

* Federn's method.

c) If necessary, the rotor is then run near its second critical speed and weights added as illustrated in Fig. 60(e). The effect of these weights is to compensate for the modal unbalance, but will not disturb either the couple balancing of Figs. 60(b) and 60(c) since the resulting moments about the centre line are equal to zero, or the balancing of Fig. 60(d).

The object of balancing the flexural modes is to reduce the deflection of the shaft at the critical speeds by balancing out the forces which produce the deflection, or in effect to reduce the corresponding bending moment diagram to a negligible amount.

Most manufacturers would probably agree that modal balancing should be carried out when the rotor is in the turbine on its true supports, and when the rotor has attained a steady temperature. This is difficult to achieve, however, because of the need to lift the top-half casing to be able to put weights in some other balancing plane.

Another problem is that of running the rotor at high rotational speeds, due to windage problems, unless a partial-vacuum chamber is constructed.

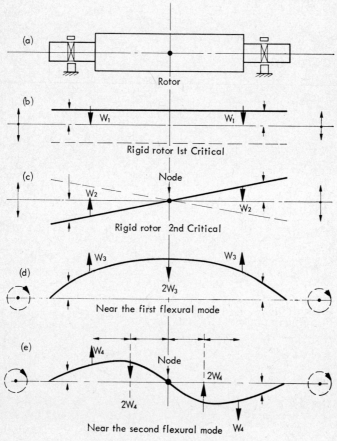

(a) Rotor

(b) W_1 W_1

Rigid rotor 1st Critical

(c) Node

W_2 W_2

Rigid rotor 2nd Critical

(d) W_3 W_3

$2W_3$

Near the first flexural mode

(e) W_4 Node $2W_4$

$2W_4$

Near the second flexural mode W_4

FIG. 60.—*Balancing flexible rotors.*

12.4. OIL WHIRL (OIL WHIP)

Rotor vibration can also be caused by what is termed "oil whirl" or "oil whip" (through modern turbines usually have short, highly loaded bearings to avoid such phenomena).

Some manufacturers fit anti-whirl bearings as standard equipment in modern turbines, though the type fitted varies from one manufacturer to another.

Oil film whirl is a self-excited vibration which is characterized by a circular or elliptical motion of the shaft journal within an oil film lubricated journal bearing, generally occurring at the shaft half-order frequency (one complete cycle for every two revolutions of the shaft).

One authority* has suggested that rotor unbalance vibration alone or in combination with oil film excitation, may cause instability at a frequency which is exactly one-half, or one-third rotational frequency, and that the phenomenon can be corrected or reduced to by sufficiently good rotor balancing.†

The upper limit of whirling frequency for an idealized unloaded bearing is $w = \Omega/2$ where w is the oil-film whirling frequency and Ω is the shaft rotational frequency.

For a flexible rotor in rigid bearings, if its natural transverse frequency (critical speed) is less than the upper limit of oil-film whirl, the system is usually unstable.

By increasing the bearing load using short bearings, (and increasing the side leakage) the upper limit may be reduced to $w = \Omega/3$. It would appear therefore that highly flexible bearing supports and oil film flexibility which depressed the calculated shaft critical frequency (based on rigid bearings) in combination with bearings which have an upper limit of bearing oil-film whirl frequency equal to one-half the rotational speed, could well be an unstable combination, and might explain why some manufacturers chose to fit anti-whirl bearings as standard equipment.

The problem of oil whirl is not a clear-cut phenomenon, and although many papers have been written on the subject, not all authors agree on the actual mechanism. It is quite possible that a number of mysterious cases of rotor vibration in recent years may have been caused by oil whirl, despite the provision of short, highly loaded bearings.

---

* "Self-induced Vibrations" by J. G. Baker, Trans ASME, Vol. 55, 1933, paper APM-55-2, Sect. 13.
† The influence of oil-film journal bearings on the stability of rotating machines by A. C. Hagg (App. Mech. Div.) presented at Annual Meeting, N.Y., Nov. 26–29, 1945 of ASME.

13. MEASUREMENTS AND LIMITS
OF VIBRATION

13.1. TERMS AND DEFINITIONS

Vibration velocity "V" in mm/sec has been adopted as the standard form of measurement for vibratory levels in steam turbine machinery.

In the case of sinusoidal vibrations where $V = \hat{V} \cos \omega t$ and also in the case of vibrations consisting of several components at different frequencies, the root-mean-square value (V_{eff}) of the vibration velocity "V" is the characteristic value for the vibration strength.

The value V_{eff} can be measured directly by electrical instruments provided with a square law characteristic of velocity indication.

If the non-harmonic, periodic or non-periodic vibrations are in recorded form, the effective value of the velocity must be formed as a root-mean-square value of the instantaneous value $V(t)$ according to the following formula:

$$V_{\text{eff}} = \sqrt{\frac{1}{T} \int_0^T V^2(t)\, dt}$$

If the vibration trace has been analysed into components of amplitudes $\hat{S}_1$, $\hat{S}_2$, etc., with corresponding angular frequencies ω_1, ω_2, etc., then

$$V_{\text{eff}} = \sqrt{\tfrac{1}{2}(\hat{S}_1^2 \omega_1^2 + \hat{S}_2^2 \omega_2^2 + \text{etc.}}$$

or

$$V_{\text{eff}} = \sqrt{\tfrac{1}{2}(V_1^2 + V_2^2 + \text{etc.}}$$

In practice a recorded vibratory trace may show a predominantly single sinusoidal wave form and a fair assessment of the velocity of vibration may be obtained by measuring this predominant wave form amplitude and frequency from the trace. Then

$$V_{\text{eff}} = \frac{1}{\sqrt{2}} \cdot \hat{S} \cdot \frac{(2\pi N)}{(60)}$$

where

N = frequency in cycles per minute.
$\hat{S} = \tfrac{1}{2} \times$ peak to peak trace width in mm $\times 10^{-3}$ (the single amplitude in mm $\times 10^{-3}$).

13.2. MEASURING INSTRUMENTS

The vibration measured on the bearing keeps can be indicated or recorded with either mechanically or electrically operated instruments.

Ideally, the measuring instrument should consist of a vibration pick-up with speed-monitoring mechanical/electrical converter and an indicator with a square law characteristic.

Instruments with linear characteristics such as linearly operating surface-contact rectifiers can produce inaccurate readings in the case of mixed frequency vibrations. These should be used only if there is a predominantly sinusoidal wave form having small mixed components.

The linear working frequency range of the measuring instrument must be wide enough for all the freqeuncy components which are needed for the evaluation of the vibration level to be indicated without distortion of amplitude. Its range of modulation and environmental stability must correspond to the measuring conditions in question.

To exclude the possibility that vibrations normal to the direction of measurement will distort the indication of the vibrations in the direction of measurement, the vibration pickup must be sufficiently direction sensitive.

The error limits of each individual measurement are in addition affected by the coupling between the pick-up and the object being measured, and also by the reaction of the pick-up on the object. To keep the measuring error as small as possible, good coupling is important and a device should be used whose resonant mass represents only a few per cent of the local vibrating mass under consideration. A mass ratio of $\frac{1}{10}$ should in no circumstances be exceeded.

Measurements should preferably be carried out at the points where the vibration energy is transmitted to the mounting or to other parts. In the case of steam turbines the points of measurement should be on the bearing housing (keeps) in the horizontal direction at a height corresponding to the shaft centreline, vertically above the centre of the shaft centreline in the middle of the housing, and axially parallel to the shaft axis at shaft height.

Figure 61 is a graph of amplitude in $mm \times 10^{-3}$ versus frequency in cycles per second, with a cross plot of vibration velocity (V_{eff}) in mm/sec RMS.

Bands of vibration levels are denoted Good, Operational condition, Allowable, and Not allowable, which are terms which take into account the three quantities, frequency, amplitude, and velocity of vibration.

13.3. THE V.D.I. RECOMMENDATION ON VIBRATION LIMITS

The graph Fig. 61 is taken from the V.D.I. Directive 2056 of October 1964, machinery group T, and is generally considered to give the most suitable limiting vibration levels in marine steam turbines to date.

In Fig. 62 the various levels of vibration velocity (V_{eff}) used by manufacturers is portrayed. There is no hard and fast rule for the limits employed, but the majority of manufacturers use the V.D.I. Directive 2056 (T) as a basis for alarming or tripping or both.

13.4. VIBRATION LIMITS USED BY VARIOUS MANUFACTURERS

G.E. (USA) have made a strong plea for acceleration measurements in place of velocity at the bearing caps on the basis that this value will be directly related to the forces acting in the system. They have also stated that they are currently developing monitoring equipment based on acceleration measurements.

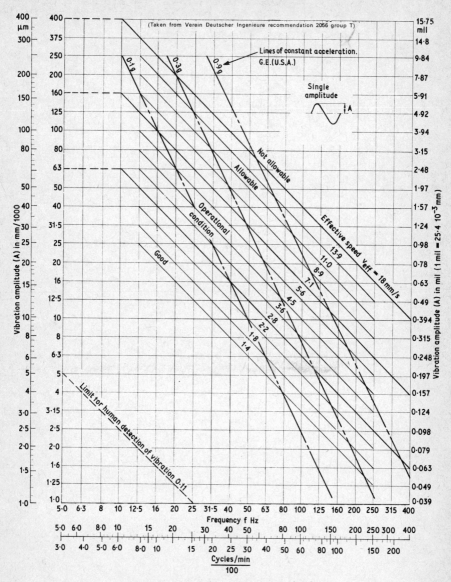

FIG. 61.—*Manufacturer's vibration levels.*

In fact G.E. (USA) have set limits of acceleration at 0·3 g for the alarm level, and 0·9 g as the danger level. In Fig. 61 lines of constant acceleration are illustrated for 0·1 g, 0·3 g and 0·9 g, from which it can be seen that for an HP turbine, for example, rotating at 6000 rev/min, a once per revolution (first order) vibration corresponding to 100 Hz

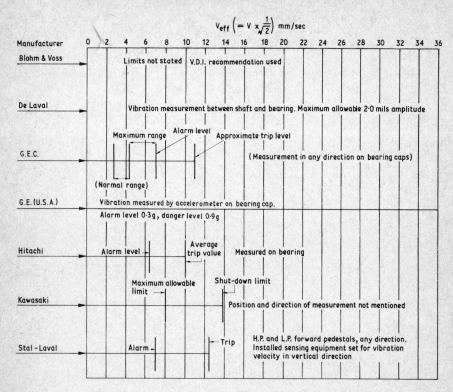

FIG. 62.—*Limits of vibration used by various manufacturers.*

would be equivalent to $7·45 \times 10^{-3}$ mm single amplitude, and a vibration velocity of $V_{eff} = 3·31$ mm/sec, which appears to be a relatively low alarm level compared with other manufacturers (Fig. 62). At lower turbine speeds however, and assuming again a first order vibratory force, the $0·3$ g alarm level would be equivalent to a higher vibration velocity.

Suppose, for example, that the HP rotor first critical speed occurred at about 50 per cent of the maximum speed, a first order vibratory force (unbalanced, or bowed rotor) at 50 Hz would give the equivalent of $29·8 \times 10^{-3}$ mm (S.A.) and a vibration velocity of $V_{eff} = 6·62$ mm/sec for an acceleration level of $0·3$ g. This vibration velocity equivalent is very close to the alarm limits employed by other turbine manufacturers (Fig. 62).

It is perfectly valid to specify an amplitude of vibration, provided it is applied at a particular rotor speed, such that the equivalent velocity of vibration is within acceptable limits, and that a seismic pick-up is used to measure the vibration on the bearing keeps.

H. G. Yates in 1949 showed clearly that velocity is the most suitable unit of vibration measurement, which "will result in similar values for all machinery of the same type, and constructed with the same degree of precision".

It is debatable whether a maximum allowable level of vibration should automatically trip the main turbine, or reduce speed under automatic control, since this is largely dependent upon the limit chosen for the maximum allowable vibration.

The scope of the book does not permit a lengthy discourse on the subject, but there is clearly a need for research into acceptable levels of vibration, to safeguard main steam turbines on the one hand without being overcautious on the other.

Messrs De Laval on the other hand have specified a maximum allowable limit of 2·0 mils single amplitude between shaft and bearings. If such measurements are obtained using, for example, a proximity transducer then the limits shown in the V.D.I. recommendations do not apply because the amplitudes measured are quite different quantities.

There is little doubt, however, that in the majority of cases the installation of steam turbine vibration monitoring devices has been found to be a valuable and, possibly, a vital item of equipment when used correctly and carefully maintained and calibrated.

14. TECHNICAL INVESTIGATION CASE HISTORIES

The following are a few selected cases in which the author was involved during his years as a "trouble-shooting" Technical Investigation Surveyor with Lloyds' Register of Shipping, travelling, often at very short notice to any part of the world, as one of a team of engineers able to deal with a broad spectrum of hull and machinery problems, installing and using sophisticated measuring instruments for diagnostic analysis in enginerooms and elsewhere following up with considered recommendations after analysis of results.

CASE I—TANKER. TURBO-ALTERNATOR TRIPPING OUT

The starboard turbo-alternator had tripped out causing blackout and loss of helm on two separate occasions in May and June 1965 when passing the same position in the Suez Canal, northward bound, in the loaded condition on each occasion.

After the first incident the turbine rotor shaft was found to be bent, and gear wheel and pinion were damaged.

The shaft was straightened and rebalanced, but no thermal stability tests were carried out.

On the second occasion when the set tripped out it was quickly re-set and the unit ran on no-load. After some time the vibration decreased and the set ran normally on load.

On no other occasion had the set tripped out except, when once tied up alongside, the Chief Engineer had managed to trip the unit twice in succession on no-load by rapidly turning the manual speed control wheel from minimum to fully open.

The Chief Engineer had noticed that the gland sealing segment tips were rubbed at mid-span of the rotor. He also stated that there was a small area of rusting at mid-span, about 2 in long and $\frac{1}{8}$ in wide, but not in way of the gland sealing surface.

Boiler salt content was normal each time and no carry-over noises were heard before the unit had tripped.

Although hull vibration was measured as a matter of routine investigation, there was no good reason for believing that the trip had been initiated by hull vibration in the generator flat, even in shallow water conditions, particularly as only one of the two sets had been affected.

Inspection of the control meter chart soon revealed an interesting phenomenon.

A period of some hours on standby waiting to join the northbound convoy when the steam temperature was steady at 320°C on the first occasion and 340°C on the

114

second occasion was followed by a rapid rise in steam temperature following the Pilot's request for half-ahead.

Figures 63(a) and 63(b) shows the temperature increase on the first occasion as 24°C/min and on the second occasion as 14°C/min, and as indicated in Fig. 63(a) the unit tripped when the boiler steam temperature had risen to 420°C on the starboard boiler, and 460°C on the port boiler.

There is no doubt that the sudden rise in temperature of the steam was responsible for the thermal bend which occurred, and this would be sufficient to trip the machine. The trip mechanism comprises a flat steel spring in the end of the rotor with a mass on the end (Fig. 64). When straight the bar would take up the attitude AB. A set screw bends the bar back so that the weight is offset just beyond the centreline of rotation. When the shaft overspeeds the increased centrifugal force on the weight bends the bar further and the weight knocks the trip finger L. Thus, as shown in Fig. 65, if the shaft bends, the weight is displaced from the normal offset and deflects the spring bar farther due to the increased radius of rotation of the weight at service speed, acting in the same way as a trip.

Assuming the trip is set for 10 per cent overspeed, then this represents the centrifugal force required to bend the spring further than the offset.

So, for straight shaft, C.F. at at overspeed $= m\omega_s^2(1\cdot1)^2r$ where $\omega_s =$ service speed.

$$r = \text{preset eccentricity at service speed.}$$

If $\delta r =$ increased eccentricity of weight due to a rotor bend when running at the service speed, then centrifugal force $= m\omega_s^2(r + \delta r)$

$$\therefore \frac{\delta r}{r} = 0\cdot21$$

In other words, if the end of the shaft were diplaced due to a bend in the rotor by one-fifth of the original weight offset distance, then the spring will bend and the unit will trip.

In round figures an original offset of $0\cdot020$ in will require the end of the rotor to be bent from the axis of rotation by $0\cdot004$ in to trip out.

The most likely reasons for the shaft bending due to a sudden increase in temperature was the spot of rust on the rotor surface which caused a difference in temperature across the shaft diameter. Any blemish of this nature has a different coefficient of heat transfer and surface emissivity. A sudden application of heat to the rotor will show up either any such non-uniformity of the surface or non-homogeneity of the rotor material, which the more gentle treatment (even thermal stability tests) will not normally reveal.

The fault in the boiler was probably the superheater bypass malfunctioning. Recommendations were made to examine the operation and control of the boiler, and to remove the rust on the rotor. No further trouble was reported.

14.2. CASE II—PASSENGER VESSEL TURBO-ALTERNATOR FAILURES

Inlet pressure 560 lbs/in^{2}g, inlet temperature 450°C, 9000 rev/min, built 1961, 900 kVA.

This small passenger vessel had three turbo-alternators. The port T/A had failed in May 1966, and exactly one month later in June the starboard T/A had failed. It was stated that no excessive change in load or operating conditions had occurred prior to either failure.

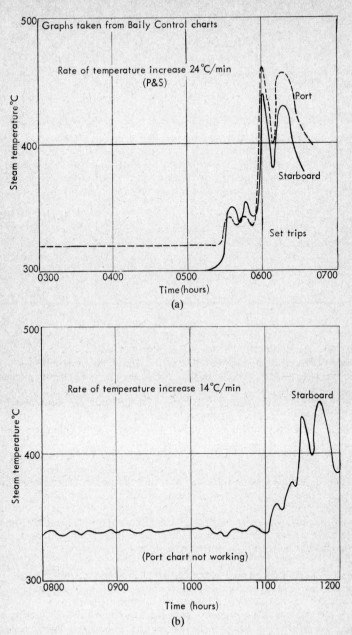

FIG. 63.—(a) Temperature increase in rotor shaft (1st occasion). (b) Temperature increase in rotor shaft (2nd occasion).

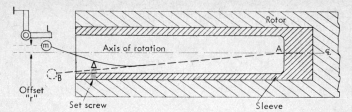

FIG. 64.—*Overspeed trip device.*

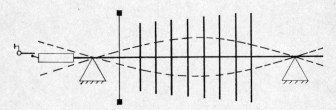

FIG. 65.—*The effect of a bend in the shaft.*

When the author arrived on board in July, the port rotor had already been crated and taken ashore, but the starboard rotor was still in position, with the top half removed.

As can be seen from the photographs, there was considerable damage caused by the failure, but of all the cases investigated, this was to prove the most interesting to piece together and eventually to locate the source of the damage through painstaking examination of every piece.

When the port rotor had been uncrated, the damaged rotor and associated bits were found to be almost identical with those of the starboard unit.

Looking at plates 1 and 2 it will be seen how remarkably similar the two damaged rotors appeared.

Again, plates 3 and 4 show the fine-tooth coupling tubes to have suffered the same damage.

The low pressure end journals had been bent, and broken off again, from plates 5 and 6, very alike on port and starboard units.

Other damage was the same for both turbines as well, the only difference being the fracture of the inlet end journal which in turn destroyed the layshaft driving the gear-type oil pumps and governor mechanism.

All blades on stages 6 and 7 had been torn off at the root, the sixth, seventh and eighth stage nozzle diaphragms had been destroyed, the interstage gland seals were flattened, the outlet end bearings were oval and right down to the steel housing, studs on the horizontal joint were stretched or sheared, the steel casting coupling housing was distorted and studs sheared, condenser tubes were sheared, and so on.

Both coupling tubes retained the coupling ring on the turbine rotor end as shown in plates 3 and 4, though they had come off the gear pinion end.

There was some evidences of sticking control valves due to relay oil contamination which may have had some significance in what was to come.

PLATE 1.—*Port turbine rotor.*

As a picture of the damage was built up, there remained one leading question. What had bent and then broken off the outlet end journals?

Had blades come off causing unbalance of the rotor, or a slug of water made the shaft bend and vibrate, hammering out the bearings, or had the sticky control valves resulted in an overspeed?

Inspection showed that the face of the coupling flange which had broken off with the bearing journal was indented with the male teeth of the coupling tube (plates 5 and 6). This could only have happened if the tube was pressed into it before the bend in the journal had developed.

The coupling oil sprayer which is fitted at the pinion end told the rest of the story, as seen in plate 7.

The bolts of the gear pinion end coupling ring were found in the gearbox, and some were found still in the coupling (plates 8 and 9). These had been sheared off. Brinell tests on the remaining pieces of coupling bolts showed the turbine end bolts to be equivalent to a tensile strength of 40 tons/in^2 and the pinion end coupling bolts 33 tons/in.^{2} A subsequent analysis showed the material to be identical, but the turbine end bolts were air-cooled or normalized, which gave them a higher tensile strength.

The centre turbo-alternator which had not been damaged was examined, and the coupling bolts removed. These showed evidence of a partial shear of the gear pinion end coupling bolts.

PLATE 2.—*Starboard turbine rotor.*

The bend in both journals was measured and is reproduced in Fig. 66 showing the final cause of the bend and subsequent failure. Briefly, the pinion end coupling bolts had sheared first, and the tube had gyrated wildly, working over the end of the oil sprayer (plate 7) pressing the other end into the outlet end flange of the rotor. The turbine end of the coupling tube had been held in place by the coupling ring circlip and when the pinion end had worked its way over the oil sprayer it had pulled the turbine flange over and bent the shaft. The tube had struck the steel casting housing and flattened the end (plates 3 and 4) the pinion end coupling ring having been thrown clear, and finally due to the enormous unbalance of the rotor at what was probably somewhere near the overspeed rev/min the end of the rotor had been torn off.

Calculations showed that the lower tensile steel bolts at the pinion end would require a torque of nearly 11 times the maximum rated torque to shear.

It was considered that faulty synchronization was the cause of the failures.

One authority confirmed that the worst case of faulty synchronization occurred when the machine was connected to the system 120° out of phase. The air-gap torque in this condition for a 600 kW alternator of $11\frac{1}{2}$ per cent reactance was 11·4 times the full-load torque by calculation. Faulty 3-phase synchronizing, faulty single-phase synchronizing and line-to-line short circuit gave torques of about the same order. The short circuit condition happened so rarely that it could be ignored in this instance.

PLATE 3.—*Port coupling tube.*

It was significant that two installations had failed in one vessel at about the same time. Since the air-gap torques in two sets during synchronization are inversely proportional to their size, these two being identical would receive the same torques. Again, the failure had occurred despite the provision of three distinct indications for synchronizing and it seemed unlikely that all three would be faulty simultaneously.

The rule requirement for Lloyd's Register is for two separate systems for synchronization of the generators. However, this vessel had three systems, the three-light system, synchroscope and an automatic synchronizing system. Manual speed regulation was necessary for all three methods. The automatic system closed the circuit-breakers only when the proper conditions of voltage and frequency were satisfied.

As mentioned previously, due to relay oil contamination, there was evidence that the steam control valves were sticking during operation. It is likely, therefore, that manual control at the switchboard could have been difficult due to the erratic response of the control valves. Under such conditions the operator using the automatic synchronization system, unaware perhaps of the control valve relay oil contamination may have thought the fault to be in the automatic synchronization system and attempted to synchronize using one of the two remaining methods neither of which would prevent the closing of the circuit-breakers if the turbo-generators were not synchronized.

PLATE 4.—*Starboard coupling tube.*

There are other possible causes of faulty synchronization, but in view of the failure of two sets in the short space of one month and indications of the third having been subjected to a large torque, sticking control valves resulting in faulty synchronization seems to be the most reasonable explanation.

14.3. CASE III—PASSENGER VESSEL LP TURBINE BLADE FAILURES

The vessel had a long history of troubles which began four years before the author attended on board.

Most of the troubles were confined to the LP rotor and gearing, and were too lengthy and confused to be mentioned here in full. During the trial in 1964 reblading of the last LP stage had just been completed. Various other repairs had been carried out, and a trial voyage was intended both to test the repairs and to measure turbine vibration and noise levels of the gearing train.

The Chief Engineer designed and built a "blade guard" round the bottom half casing in way of the downward flow steam exhaust area of the LP turbine to stop the recurrent problem of pierced condenser tubes.

Although the author and his colleague expressed some doubts about partial blockage of the steam flow path, some sympathy was felt for his solution to the problem.

PLATE 5.—*Port turbine rotor coupling flange.*

The blade guard consisted of two half-rings joined sideways by metal plating to form a semi-circular grid under the rotor outlet end. The plates were about $\frac{5}{16}$ in thick by 3 in wide by 12 in long and welded at the ends to the rings. The space at both sides of the exhaust were covered by two pieces of $\frac{1}{2}$ in thick steel with holes drilled in them to allow the passage of steam.

On the return leg of the voyage while measurements were being carried out on the starboard LP turbine, the port LP turbine suddenly failed. The set was shut down quickly, but not before considerable damage had been done.

On opening up the port LP turbine it was found that a whole packet of seven blades had torn free from their root fixings, and as can be seen in plate 10, some of the spacers had been torn loose, some had remained; a case of poor fitting and poor brazing of the root spacers and blades.

One of the lessons to be learnt from this particular failure is that the installation of the "blade guard" which was intended to protect the condenser tubes did more harm than good, because the blades which came away bounced off the specially constructed guard on to the adjacent last row of the astern wheel damaging those blades as well (plate 11) and with the added impetus forced a way through the blade guard (plate 12) and pierced the condenser tubes once again.

Plate 13 is a view of the aft end bearing keep top half showing the fracture all the way along the flange. The unbalanced rotor was contained by the top half LP casing, for the bearing keep would not have been sufficient to retain it alone. Incidentally, a noise level of 115 dB was measured in way of the port gearbox, which did nothing to improve the environment in the engine room.

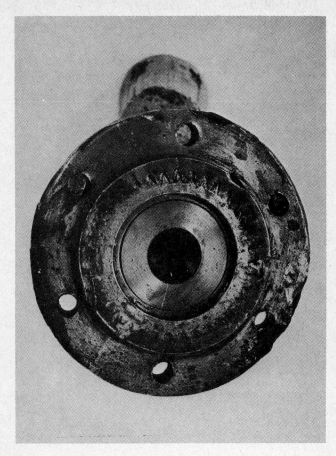

PLATE 6.—*Starboard turbine rotor coupling flange.*

14.4. TANKER. LP TURBINE BLADE EROSION

Maximum shp 22 000, 108 rev/min, 41 kg/cm^2, 450°C at inlet (590 lbs/in^2, 840°F). (Not to L.R. Class).

Reaction turbine: HP turbine, Curtis wheel plus 18 50 per cent reaction stages; LP turbine, double-flow reaction, 22 stages per flow.

The investigation was concerned with the extensive erosion of the last six stages in both flows of the LP turbine.

This was a particularly difficult case because the ship had changed hands just after building and the previous owners had uprated the maximum power from 20 000 to 22 000 shp during building. The boiler, however, was already installed in the vessel when the new engine capacity was called for, and although very little information was available with regard to the boiler, it was alleged that some modifications had been made to the boiler, but no details were forthcoming. From an examination of the log book it

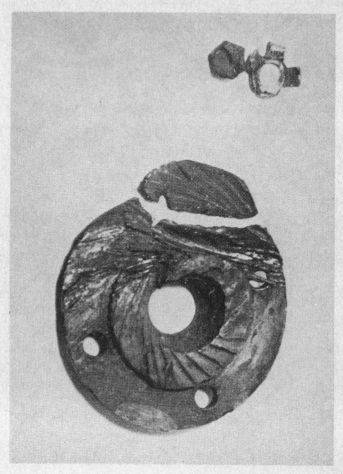

PLATE 7.—*Damaged oil spray, screw head and locking washer.*

appeared that for most of the time the main engines were not developing full or even the normal service power. The owners stated that in order to maintain full superheat temperature with the auxiliaries working they developed only 17 000 shp.

Furthermore, the vessel did not achieve the full superheat temperature on trials. At 20 000 shp superheat temperature was 430°C, but the ship had been accepted because it was not appreciated that erosion would occur at the lower superheat temperature.

The ship was run at reduced revolutions and lower superheat temperature than the turbine had been designed for, and it was estimated that for most of the time the last stages were running approximately 13 to 14 per cent wet instead of the 9 to 10 per cent for which they had been originally designed.

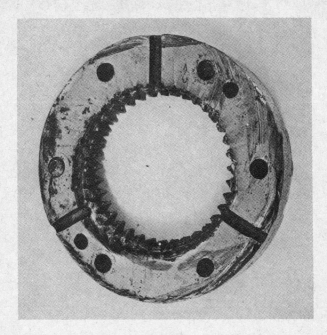

PLATE 8.—*Port turbine coupling ring.*

This would account for the number of stages affected, no doubt, for the higher the percentage of wetness in the last stage, the greater the number of stages affected upstream.

The curves in Figs. 67(a) and 67(b) show the relationship for this turbine of pressure, temperature and condenser vacuum on percentage of wetness for the nineteenth and twenty-second stages, respectively.

It is clear that the most significant effect is that of superheater temperature, pressure being less significant. It is also clear that the last few stages are more affected by condenser vacuum than those further upstream.

From an examination of the log book it was seen that some period of time (particularly during the 12–4 a.m. watch) was spent steaming with an inlet temperature of 390°C and pressure 497 lbs/in²abs whilst the vacuum was 97·2 per cent. This corresponds to about 13·6 per cent wetness in the last stage.

There were further complications concerning the auxiliaries.

The Chief Engineer stated that superheater temperatures were difficult to maintain during a passage in the Gulf. With air conditioning, refrigeration, and both fixed speed circulating pumps operating, the total electrical load was beyond the capacity of one turbo-generator.

For this reason, therefore, he usually ran the second turbo-generator in parallel with the first. The increase in steam throughput was additionally responsible for the reduction in superheater outlet temperature.

PLATE 9.—*Starboard turbine coupling ring.*

A number of other defects were found such as:
a) Blocked bleed belt drains, on both the forward and aft flows of the double-flow LP turbine.
b) Pieces broken off the HP turbine inlet nozzle trailing edges measuring about 1 cm square.
c) Superheater thermocouples non-operative. Mercury in steel thermometers were used instead, and one was reading high by 20°C. The location of these indicators was at the side of the boiler some 15 ft to 20 ft above the boiler operating flat.
d) The mercury in steel thermometer at the HP turbine outlet was reading 290°C when the casing was at ambient temperature.
    The depth of erosion measured from the leading edge over a period of $4\frac{1}{2}$ years, which is shown in Fig. 68, would appear to be stabilizing, but due to the proximity of the lacing wire holes the owners were advised to have them replaced.
    The erosion damage in the last rows of the forward flow can be seen in plate 14.
    It is thought that this trend of stabilization is due to two factors.
1) The axial distance from fixed blade trailing edge to moving blade leading edge is increased, and gives the droplets that much more time to accelerate and reach a velocity nearer that of the steam.
2) The jagged leading edge surface retains some of the water and cushions droplet impact.

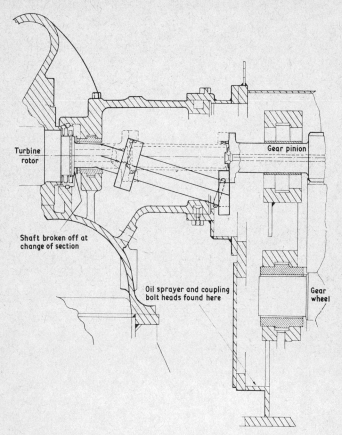

FIG. 66.—*Diagrammatic sketch showing likely manner in which turbine shaft was bent following shear failure of gear pinion coupling bolts.*

Erosion of this kind is not usual in modern machines and if such a case is found it will be because of operation at low superheater outlet temperature, or low temperature combined with low inlet pressure, and high vacuum.

A survey of classed vessels over a period from 1952 to 1966 showed only eight vessels in 600 to 700 had experienced serious erosion in the first 24 months of service, six of these were serious within 12 months of service, and three vessels of the six were double-flow reaction turbines.

Only four of the eight vessels had to have repairs, the remainder stabilized and were satisfactory.

Slagging or sooting of superheater tubes will depress the outlet temperature and a reduction of 8°C to 14°C is not uncommon, as a result of the grade of fuel oil burned combined with the impracticability of cleaning superheater tubes at frequent intervals.

Present day designs of special tapered and twisted last stage blades minimize erosion, with provision for moisture removal through water extraction channels.

PLATE 10.—*Last row ahead. One packet of blades thrown out.*

14.5. CASE V—TANKER. HP ROTOR VIBRATION

31 500 shp at 80 rev/min. (Not to LR Class), HP rotor speed 6400 rev/min.

This case is the classic rotor vibration incident resulting from a bent shaft run near the critical speed and hammering out the bearings.

The vessel had completed a first trial, and was on the second trials in order to prove burners and various auxiliaries which had previously given trouble.

In the early morning it was stated that revolutions were decreased to 25 rev/min to calibrate the torsion meter.

Again, the facts were difficult to establish conclusively, but in the author's opinion there was an ingress of water through the first bled steam belt on to the hot rotor at low rev/min, although it is conceivable that the shaft may have been stopped for some time during the calibration and a bend in the rotor initiated.

When the main engine was run up again the vibration built up from 35–40 propeller rev/min, until at about 40–50 rev/min, a heavy rub developed, bending the shaft further and finally hammering out the white metal bearing surface, and running on the steel backing of the forward bearing. The aft bearing white metal was hammered and cracked but otherwise undamaged. The Curtis wheel was badly damaged and there was a permanent bend in the rotor of 0·005 in at 180° to the position of the rub. (This is consistent with observed shaft rubbing phenomena.) The vibration was not noticed in the sound-proofed control room above the turbine flat until the rotor had begun to

PLATE 11.—*View showing damage to astern wheel blades.*

hammer out the bearings, since there was no vibration monitoring equipment fitted to the HP or LP turbines.

The manufacturers stated that the critical whirling speed of the HP rotor shaft was 4000 rev/min to 4500 rev/min, making due allowances for bearing oil film stiffness and bearing support stiffness. (48 rev/min to 54 rev/min on the propeller shaft.) Once a bend is initiated it develops further with turbine rev/min, and since the first critical speed is below the service speed, it will peak in amplitude, limited only by the diaphragm interstage glands and oil damping. The glands if spring-backed will bottom, cause heavy rubbing and finally heat the shaft until it becomes permanently bent. There is no alternative then but to remove the shaft and attempt to straighten it. On the other hand, a bend in the shaft due to thermal distortion (such as failing to turn the shaft with the turning gear when steam is shut off) if noticed in time at low rev/min before a significant rub has developed, can be straightened merely by turning the shaft on steam for a period of some hours at very low rev/min. This will heat the shaft uniformly and usually remove

PLATE 12.—*View showing buckled guard.*

the bend. The turbine can then be slowly taken up to speed while watching the vibration monitoring equipment.

In the case considered here it was estimated that had the centre of gravity of the rotor been displaced by 0·0027 in the centrifugal force would be equal to the weight of the rotor at 45 propeller rev/min. The displacement of the CG of the rotor would, of course, depend on the flexural shape of the bend developed, but there is no doubt that the amplitude of the vibration was many times greater than 0·0027 in, in view of the heavy rub. Besides, the permanent bend in itself was 0·005 in which usually represents a small proportion of the bend when whirling.

From the damage to the bearings it had evidently bent more towards the forward end.

The cause of the bend was not definitely established because the author was not called in until some days later, but as already stated the most likely reason for the bend was ingress of water to the shaft through the faulty check valve in the first stage bled steam belt.

PLATE 13.—*Aft LP bearing keep, showing crack along flange.*

The check valve was of the hand-operated non-return type. The valve bobbin was light-spring loaded to operate as a normal non-return valve, but a hand-wheel spindle could close the valve tight. Unfortunately the end of the spindle was not chamfered, and due to excessive tightening it had "mushroomed" and jammed onto the bobbin.

When the valve was opened by hand, the bobbin had lifted off the seating against the spring pressure and was open, allowing steam into the feed heater line above the turbine flat. The feed heater valve was closed so steam was passing into the vertical leg of the pipe, condensing, and running back into the turbine at low rev/min filling the bleed belt and finally spilling out into the casing and being carried up to the rotor surface. The water in the bleed belt would cause the casing to hog as well, and thus make any tendency to rub more severe.

When the author went out on the third trial a replacement rotor had been fitted in the repaired casing.

Vibration measurements on the bearing keeps were carried out under varying operating conditions and the vibration level never exceeded 3·0 mm/sec RMS velocity

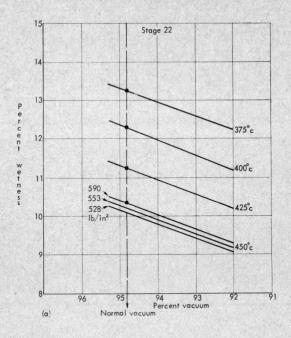

(a)

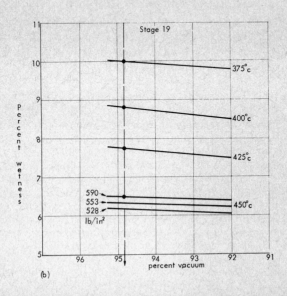

(b)

Fig. 67.—(a) and (b) Relation between wetness, pressure and temperature.

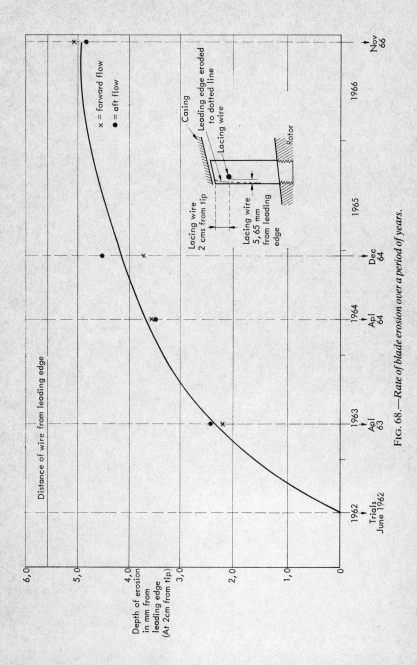

FIG. 68.—Rate of blade erosion over a period of years.

PLATE 14.—*Erosion of last stage blades in forward flow.*

(3·0 mm/sec RMS) which was quite satisfactory according to the manufacturer's limits of vibration for that rotor.

14.6. CASE VI—TANKER. HP TURBINE FINAL ROW BLADE FAILURES
    28 000 shp, 85 rev/min.

During a scheduled voyage it was reported that the vibration of the HP turbine increased over eight days from 1·0 mm/secRMS to 4·0 mm/secRMS and finally to

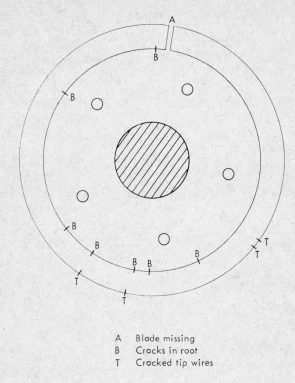

A   Blade missing
B   Cracks in root
T   Cracked tip wires

FIG. 69.—*Positions of blade failures.*

10.0 mm/secRMS on the last day.

When the casing top half was removed, one blade of 59·5 mm in length had broken away leaving the root in place and ten other blades were found with cracks in the same position (Fig. 69). Two blades of the ten had fractures in more than 95 per cent of the cross-section and were finally contained by the shrouding wire. The blade which had broken free had also been contained in place for some time even though it had failed at the root, as evident from damage to the nozzles. The failures had all occurred at the junction between the blade root shank and the bulb (Fig. 70) and had initiated on the corner of the shank in way of the blade leading edge (Fig. 71). The failure was due to metal fatigue, and some evidence of fretting was found near the start of the crack (though not at the point of initiation).

An examination of the frequencies by the author established that the most likely cause of failure was steam excitation of the clamped-pinned mode of vibration, and subsequent work confirmed the diagnosis. (It is interesting to note that this mode of vibration was responsible for the blade failures on the *Queen Elizabeth 2* two months previous to this case.)

The position of failure in the root also confirmed the author's opinion that under operating conditions the root became an extension of the blade and took part in the vibration of the blade profile length. Frequencies of vibration must always be calculated

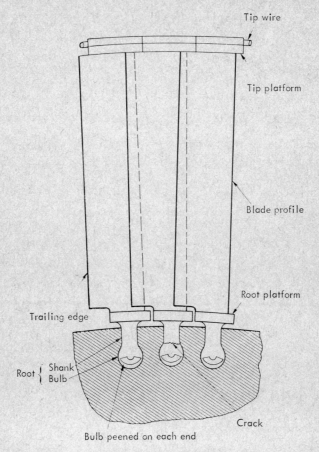

FIG. 70.—*Position of crack.*

assuming this condition. The root shank was clear of the slot by about 0·0010 in, and one could be forgiven for considering the root as "tight" and not capable of vibration, but when one considers that at frequencies of 4500 c/s the maximum amplitude of vibration at about mid-height of the blades is probably not much more than about 0·002 in to 0·003 in, the root amplitude will be extremely small by comparison. Furthermore, it is not unreasonable that the bulb was not stationary in the wheel, but oscillated within the hole containing it. This would account for the fretting seen on the bulb surface at the points of highest load-bearing under centrifugal loading. Since the bulb is peened at the ends to fasten it tightly into the hole, one could again be forgiven for considering that with the additional centrifugal load the bulb would not move. Movements, however, occur on a microscopic scale.

     Blade vibration is acceptable provided the maximum stress does not exceed the safety limit of stress reversals based on some measured metal fatigue limit. In the case

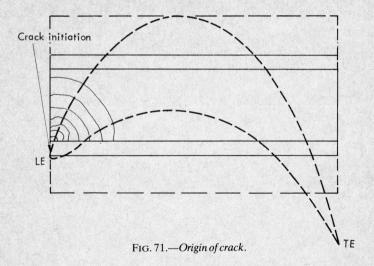

Crack initiation

LE

TE

FIG. 71.—*Origin of crack*.

under discussion the maximum stress was greater than the calculated value, due to an under-estimation of the exciting force.

In order to measure the exciting force the manufacturers devised a test under actual steaming conditions with strain gauges located on the blade at mid-height. This experiment was probably the first of its kind, for which due credit must be given to the manufacturers. They intended to calculate the swinging-form deflection of the blade and thus relate the stress at mid-height to stress in the root according to the calculated bending moment diagram. This method would again rely on interpretation of the correct swinging form. To measure the corresponding stress in the root the author initiated tests at the Society's research laboratory on a packet of three blades. By placing gauges at the blade mid-height and a series of microscopic gauges on the root, it was possible to excite the blades in the clamped-pinned mode statically and obtain the stress ratio when the blades were vibrating in the correct swinging form deflections. The results confirmed that the steam exciting force was sufficient to cause failure in the root shank under operating conditions at a frequency close to the service speed. To overcome the problem a slightly longer blade was fitted (with a lower resonant frequency) and an increase in the number of fixed nozzles from 50 to 64, thereby reducing the shaft speed at which resonance occurred, which in turn was at a lower stress level.

From the Campbell diagram shown in Fig. 72, both the steam bending and centrifugal stresses were reduced from (maximum stress) $\times (0{\cdot}995)^2$ to (maximum stress) $\times (0{\cdot}715)^2$, i.e. stresses were reduced to $51\frac{1}{2}$ per cent of the stress when the blades failed.

This particular case led to the owner's request for the author to undertake an analysis of blading in their Newbuilding vessels with particular reference to the likelihood of failure in the clamped-pinned mode.

Based on the information which was obtained from the tests during the first investigation, the author was able to show that one stage could be at risk in three Newbuilding vessels, and the owner requested modified diaphragms to avoid blade resonance.

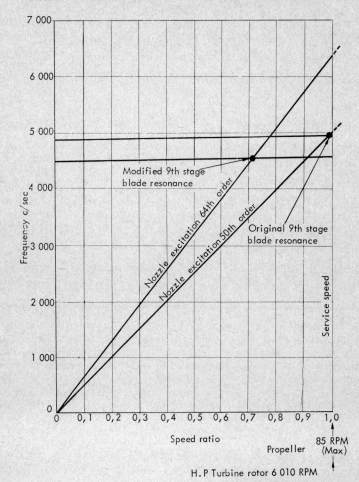

Fig. 72.—Campbell diagram of the 9th stage HP blade.

The author was recently invited to examine the blade characteristics of a second series of Newbuildings for the same owner, but it is of interest to note that no severe blade vibration characteristics were found in the second Newbuilding series of vessels. A larger frame size turbine is employed in which the power output is in the lower area of the power range covered by that particular frame size, thus all the steam bending stresses are lower and centrifugal stresses slightly lower because shorter blades and nozzles are employed and the steam throughput is reduced.

14.7 CASE VII—Q.E.2 HP TURBINE BLADE FAILURES

Twin screw. 52 000 shp screw maximum.

Blade root fixing is an important aspect when considering the vibration characteristics of blading. The manufacturing department must work together with the Stress engineer and designers if the end product (a reliable turbine blade) is to result.

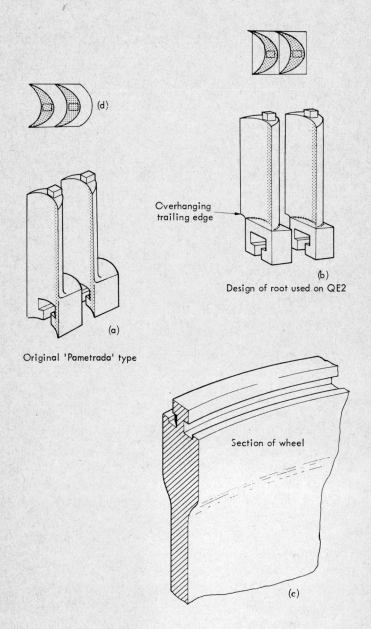

FIG. 73.—*Blade root fixing. (a) Original "Pametrada" type. (b) Design of root used on QE2.*
(c) Section of wheel.

A classic case of the division was evident during the *Queen Elizabeth 2* investigation. The "Pametrada" design of roots was of the profiled root face type. Figure 73(a) is a sketch showing the blade and root, and the integral spacer which butts against the adjoining blade. The profile must be radially angled to ensure that when fitted on the curve of the wheel rim (Fig. 73(c)), the faces do not leave any gaps. In the final fitting the root faces have to be "blued" to ensure correct bedding of the blades one against the other. This is a laborious fitting job and the manufacturing department decided that if the root faces were flat, machining of the angle between flat faces would be more accurate, and consequently the fitting would be quicker. Unfortunately, the rectangular section of the root could not contain the complete blade profile owing to the angle of the chord line unless the rectangular root section were made deeper. This would mean that fewer blades could be used per wheel resulting in larger bending stresses, etc. Their solution, therefore, was to have an overhanging trailing edge (Fig. 73(b)). The radius between the blade overhanging trailing edge and root had been filed by hand, or so it appeared, and many had sharp notches. It was at these notches that the failures originated. The replacement blades reverted to the profiled root faces, or "rhubarb" root as it is sometimes called, combined with a thickening of the blade section toward the root.

Despite the poor workmanship, the author believes that this was probably only the "straw which broke the camel's back".

The prime cause of the failures was, of course, the large static steam bending stresses combined with steam excitation of the clamped-pinned mode of vibration of the moving blades which were resonant within the operating range for stages 8 to 11 inclusive.

BIBLIOGRAPHY

1) G.E.C.B., "Mechanical (Turbines and Auxiliary Equipment)", *Modern Station Power Practice*, Vol. 3.
2) Chemistry and Metallurgy, *Modern Station Power Practice*, Vol. 5.
3) KEOGH, F. G., 1970–71. "On Load Cleaning of Steam Turbine Blading", *Proc. I. Mech. E.*, Steam Plant Group.
4) D'ARCY, N. J. H. D., 31st Parsons Memorial Lecture, "The Prospect for Steam Propulsion".
5) SMITH, D. M., 1949. "The Vibration of Blades in Packets". *Proc. 7th Intn. Congress for Applied Mechanics*, Vol. 3.
6) KANTOROWICZ, O. P. T., 1962. "Of Steam Turbine Wheel, Batch and Blade Vibrations". Excerpt from *Trans. N.E.C.I.E.S.*
7) WEAVER, F. L., and PROHL, M. A., 1958. "High Frequency Vibration of Steam-Turbine Buckets" *Trans. ASME*.
8) TAKEDA, Y., 1970. "Development of a Japanese Design Steam Turbine", *Trans. I. Mar. E.*, Vol. 82, Part 5.
9) JUNG, I. K. E., 1969. "Steam Turbine Machinery", *Trans. I. Mar. E.*, Vol: 81.
10) MOORE, L. S., 1969. "Balancing of Large Turbine Rotors", *Trans. I. Mar. E.*, Vol. 81, Part 4.
11) Fearnley and Egers Chartering Co. Ltd., 1971, Jan. "Large Tankers (over 60 000 tons deadweight)".
12) "The Case for Steam" 1970. *Shipbuilding and Shipping Record* (Special supplement), Dec.
13) DAVIS, A. W., 1971. "A Simplified Steam Plant for Marine Propulsion". *Westinghouse Engineer*, March, Vol. 31, No. 2.
14) "Evaluation Criteria for Mechanical Vibrations in Machines", 1964. *V.D.I. Recommendations 2056*, Oct.

15) COATES, J., 1970. "Combined Steam and Gas Turbines for 40 000 shp Single-screw Tankers". General Electric Second European Gas Turbine State of the Art Congress, Palma de Mallorca, May.

16) BROWNLIE, K., and YOUNG, I. T., 1969. "Research, Development and Design for Marine Propulsion Geared Steam Turbines", *Proc. IMAS '69 (London), Section 4/d*.

17) YATES, H. G., 1948 "*Vibration Diagnosis in Marine Geared Turbines*", *Trans. N.E.C.I.E.S.*, Vol. 65, pp. 225–261.

18) DONALD, K. M. B., Research and Technical Advisory Services, Lloyd's Register of Shipping, Report 2547.

19) DONALD, K. M. B., Research and Technical Advisory Services, Lloyd's Register of Shipping, Report 2833.

20) DONALD, K. M. B., and CAMPBELL, C., Research and Technical Advisory Services, Lloyd's Register of Shipping, Report 2307.

21) DONALD, K. M. B., and URWIN, K. F. G., Research and Technical Advisory Services, Lloyd's Register of Shipping, Report 2425.

22) DONALD, K. M. B., Research and Technical Advisory Services, Lloyd's Register of Shipping Report 2517.

23) FLEETING, R., and COATES, R., 1970. "Blade Failures in the HP Turbines of R.M.S. Queen Elizabeth 2" and their Rectification, *Trans. I. Mar. E.*, Vol. 82, p. 49.

24) JONES, T. P., 1972. "Design, Operating Experience and Development of Main Propulsion Epicyclic Gears", *Trans. I. Mar. E.*, Vol. 84, Part 15.

25) LARSEN, GUNNER A., 1973, "Selection of Steam Propulsion Systems for VLCC. Proc. I.Mar.E., IMAS '73 Conference (London, 4–8 June).

26) ROHDE, E. C., 1960. "Design Aspects of Modern Marine Propulsion Turbines", *SNAME*, Paper presented at the annual meeting, New York, 17–18 Nov.

27) LAST, B. P., 1964. "The Balancing of Flexible Turbine and Generator Rotors", *I.Mech.E.*, Student/Graduate Paper, Viscount Weir First Prize.

28) Ewins, D. D. J., 1973. "Vibrations Characteristics of Bladed Disc Assemblies" *Jo. of Mechanical Engineering Science*, Vol. 15., No. 3.

29) DONALD, K. M. B., 1973. "Marine Steam Turbines—Some Points of Design and Operation", *Trans. I.Mar.E.*, Vol. 85.

30) ALLEN, R. C., 1940. "Steam Turbine Blading", *Trans. ASME*, Nov.

31) TRUMPLER, W. E. Jr., and OWENS, H. M., 1955. *Trans. ASME*, 77(3).

32) KEERTON, W. J., 1958. "Steam Turbine Theory and Practice", *Sir Isaac Pitman and Sons Ltd.*, 7th Edition (text book for engineering students).

33) KROON, R. P., 1940. "Turbine-blade Vibration Due to Partial Admission", *Trans. Jo. of Applied Mechanics*, Dec.

34) WALLER, MARY D., 1938. "Vibrations of Free Circular Plates", *Proc. Physical Soc.*, Vol. 5, p. 70.

35) TRAUPE, W., 1968. Thermische Turbonaschinen, Vol. 1, 2nd Edition, *Springer*, Berlin/Heidelberg/New York.